BIGGEST BOOK OF JUST FOR BOYS

Kidsbooks®

Search & Finds®,
Mazes, Crosswords,
How to Draws,
and More!

Get ready for hours of fun—exclusively for boys!
You'll love solving puzzles and learning
how to draw activities along the way with

The Biggest Book of
Just for Boys!

If you get stumped on any of the puzzles,
don't worry—we put the answers
in the back of the book!

Boys of all ages will enjoy this activity
book—anytime and anywhere.
Start working your way through—there's
lots of awesome activities
just for boys!

Kidsbooks®

Construction Maze

Follow the path from **Start** to **Finish** to guide the boy to the end of the construction site.

Answer on page 290

Sudoku
BRAIN BUILDER

Flex those gray matter muscles and try to decode this sudoku. Fill in the empty squares so that each row, column, and square contains the numbers 1–9 only once.

		6			3		2	8
		3	4			7		
9			1			5		3
6						1	9	4
4	2	8						7
5			4			2		1
		2				7	8	
8	7			6			4	

TOOL TIME

It's time to fix stuff up! Find the names of these tools in the word search below. Look up, down, backward, forward, and diagonally.

Drill	**Sander**
Hammer	**Saw**
Level	**Screwdriver**
Nail gun	**Trowel**
Pliers	**Wrench**

```
S U G L R E W H L J L S P B
K C X S M A N Q C N S A J Q
N C R D R I L L R N E W N X
V N C E P Y X F E A E X I C
Q O O C W Y D U D I V R M M
E O X S G D E T N L F U W A
S R E I L P R L A G W S R L
H L W M M Y H I S U N P E Z
I C E Y X H Q D V N F W F U
S U U V A E J N O E O C B G
J C A M E S D M C R R Y F F
I N M C X L N L T G G L X F
N E C Q E M C I J J M I C G
R V O X Q K S W I S W I K I
```

Answer on page 290

Rockin' Rebus

Solve this rebus puzzle to discover the name of something fun where you'll find dribblers.

B + [boy digging] - XE + S + [jet plane]

- ROC + B + [kids climbing rope/wall] - W

Let's Draw a
Corvette

On a separate piece of paper, follow these simple steps using a pencil and an eraser.

1 Start by drawing the canopy, body, and tire shapes. Draw through your shapes.

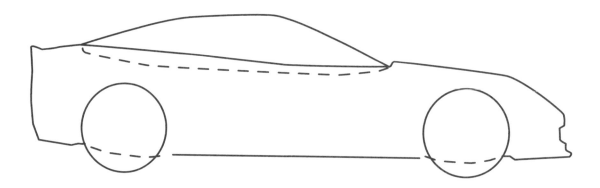

2 Erase the guidelines. Next, draw the door, wheel wells, small lights, and headlights.

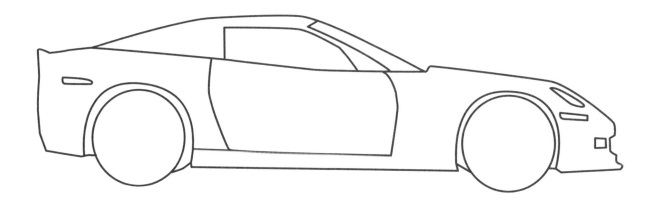

3 Add rear windows, mirrors, and rims. Use lines to show the body design.

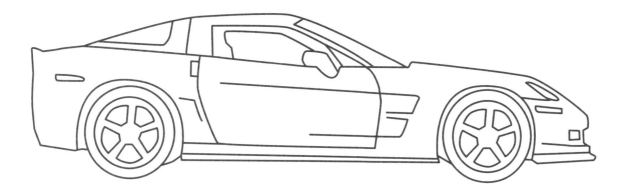

4 This Corvette looks good in purple. Add some highlights and some dark shading, a black canopy, and this car is on its way.

READY FOR THE WEEKEND

Fill in the blanks to complete this silly story about your weekend. Pick a NOUN, ADJECTIVE, or VERB from the word bank to place in a corresponding blank, or think of your own wacky words!

I can't wait for the weekend—to me it is the _____ time of the week!
[ADJECTIVE]

My favorite thing to do is _____ with my _____. My mother gets
[VERB]   [NOUN]

_____ if I _____ too much, so I try not to do that. My friends
[ADJECTIVE]   [VERB]

_____ on the weekend and I am right there with them! In the
[VERB]

blink of an eye, the weekend is over, and it's time for me to curl up in my

_____ and prep for the school week!
[NOUN]

WORD BANK

ADJECTIVES
awesome
nervous
silly
insane
magical
smart
red
straight
mushy

NOUNS
banana
ball
paper bag
t-shirt
bulldog
masterpiece
hamburger
gym shorts
jet

VERBS
sneak
pounce
jog
sleep
squat
play
borrow
drive
burp

TYPES OF ICE CREAM

Use the clues about different kinds of ice cream to solve the crossword puzzle.

ACROSS
3. Usually made with bananas
4. A mix of vanilla, chocolate, and strawberry
5. Made with ice cream, milk, and flavored syrup
7. Has a cherry on top

DOWN
1. A fruity ice cream made with only a little milk
2. A popular flavor of fruit ice cream
6. Vanilla between two cookies

Answer on page 291

Fishing
How To
TIPS

Grab your fishing pole, score some bait, and cast your reel—it's time to learn the basics of fishing. Next time you head out, you'll be a pro.

Fishing Basics

1. Pick a great location. Make sure the body of water you choose actually has FISH in it.

2. Choose your bait and hooks. Ask in your local bait shop about the size of hook you need and the type of bait, based on the type of fish you are looking to catch.

3. Cast your line and wait. If your fishing rod starts moving a lot or if you feel a pulling, odds are, you caught something. If you've been waiting for more than 20 minutes and still haven't caught anything, move on to another area.

4. Hook it. If you feel a tug on your line, jerk the line backward and up. If you have a fish, keep the line tight, pull the rod up and grab hold of the fish. Remove the hook. Do this as gently as possible.

ON THE LAKE

Find these things that have to do with boats in the word search. Look up, down, backward, forward, and diagonally.

Anchor	**Ladder**	**Marina**	**Paddle**	**Radio**
Dock	**Life jacket**	**Outrigger**	**Propeller**	**Sail**

```
O Y X G X F P J U L T E D M
F N D Q T Q M Q N G P B G P
O W J E T T S P E Z Y P R A
L A N C H O R Q R O W W K D
Q I O D X U I A K P J E P D
O I F N O N T L Z I H P A L
R U S E E C H A N Q R O I E
E Q T A J E K V C O T I K L
D F C R I A J M P X R D S W
D T V M I L C E A M V A M J
A P G I F G L K W R Z R M F
L D B N B L G S E R I D U D
O X I P E K X E G T L N N W
A L M R C H J P R Y H P A L
```

Scary Dragon

Roar! Can you find the two pictures that are exactly alike?

Answer on page 291

•List Your Big Dreams

You have to have goals, dude! List your goals here—and check them off as you get them done!

By the time I am 10,
I hope to:

By the time I am 30,
I hope to:

By the time I am 15,
I hope to:

By the time I am 40,
I hope to:

By the time I am 20,
I hope to:

Are You a Sports Fanatic?

	TRUE	FALSE
1. I have more than five sports trophies in my room.	◯	◯
2. I can calculate an ERA.	◯	◯
3. Gym is my favorite subject.	◯	◯
4. I prefer my football to a guitar.	◯	◯
5. I spend more time on a field than I do anywhere else.	◯	◯
6. I know who Michael Jordan is.	◯	◯
7. I love wearing a uniform.	◯	◯

	TRUE	FALSE

8. I have been on more than five sports teams in my life. ◯ ◯

9. I will always watch a sporting event instead of a cartoon. ◯ ◯

10. My heroes are all athletes. ◯ ◯

11. I spend more than five hours a week playing sports. ◯ ◯

TRUE

If you chose mostly "True" answers, you are a sports fanatic! You love everything about sports and are into all different types. You may enjoy other stuff, but nothing as much as football, baseball, soccer, etc.

FALSE

If you chose mostly "False" answers, you are not a sports fanatic! You tend to have other interests that you love way more than any sport, and that's cool, too.

Sudoku
SUPER SMART

Put on your thinking cap and try to decode this sudoku. Fill in the empty squares so that each row, column, and square contains the numbers 1–9 only once.

3			5			6		
			6		9	1	3	8
				1		4	2	
			9					
9	4		1		5		8	2
					7			
	8	7		5				
5	1	6	4		8			
		9			6			1

Answer on page 291

Would You Rather...

Which would you rather do?
Look at each pair of options. Think about them and check the things you would like best. Ask your friends, too!

Would you rather every day be...

☐ Christmas   or   ☐ Halloween?

Would you rather be...

☐ A shark   or   ☐ A dinosaur?

Would you rather live...

☐ In the past   or   ☐ In the future?

Would you rather own...

☐ A toy factory   or   ☐ A car factory?

Write Your

What was the best day you ever had so far? What made it such a memorable day? Write a blog entry about it here!

Best Day Ever!

Caption your picture _____

_____

_____

_____

_____

_____

_____

_____

_____

_____

_____

post by_____ time _____

Ready for Rebus

Solve this rebus puzzle to discover a fun place to go on weekends.

_ _ _ _ _ _ _

_ _ _ _ _ _ _ _

Shining Stars
FACTS

How cool is it when the night sky is clear and you can see tons and tons of stars? Here's some info on what to look for amongst the stars!

Star Bright

A constellation is a group of stars up in the sky.

Stars move around in the sky. The ONLY star that never moves is Polaris, better known as the North Star. It's located right above the North Pole. If you ever get lost, locate the North Star. It's location is always NORTH.

Little Dipper

The Little Dipper is a constellation shaped like an egg dipper or a spoon. The star at the very top of the Little Dipper is the North Star. The best way to find the North Star is to locate the Little Dipper.

Big Dipper

The Big Dipper is usually the easiest constellation to find because all the stars are really bright. It is also called "Ursa Major," which means "Big Bear" in Latin, because people used to say it looked like a bear.

Fun Facts!

- There are hundreds of constellations. Collectively, they are referred to as the Zodiac.
- The sun is actually a star. It is the star that is closest to Earth.
- Most stars are between one and ten billion years old.

Safari Animals

Are you a super seeker? Put your eyes to the test and see if you can find 10 differences between the picture on the top and the one on the bottom.

Answer on page 292

Sundae Maze

Follow the correct path through the maze to get the man to the ice-cream sundae. What's the correct path, you ask? It's the one that is made up of bananas only!

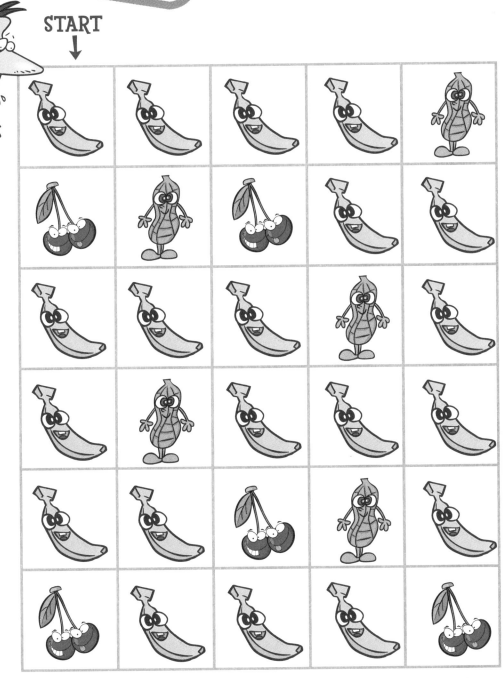

START

FINISH

MY FIRST CAR

Fill in the blanks to complete this silly story about your future first car. Pick a NOUN, ADJECTIVE, or VERB from the word bank to place in a corresponding blank, or think of your own wacky words!

My first car is going to be a _____ and it is going to be totally
[NOUN]

_____! I'm going to _____ it every single chance I get. I'll
[ADJECTIVE]   [VERB]

definitely get the _____ model so that everyone will _____
[ADJECTIVE]   [VERB]

when they set their eyes on it. My trunk will have a _____ in it.
[NOUN]

I can't wait for the day I get my driver's license! Once I pass the driving

test, I'll be sure to _____ by all my friends in my _____ car.
[VERB]   [ADJECTIVE]

WORD BANK

ADJECTIVES
pink
shiny
muddy
little
sparkly
enormous
crooked
weird
smelly

NOUNS
lemon
tank
box
puppy
missile
taxi
tricycle
dump
sock

VERBS
rev
slide
swim
fart
scream
hide
sneeze
steer
drive

School Trip

Honk! Can you find the two pictures that are exactly alike?

Answer on page 292

Would You Rather...

Sure, you have a favorite kind of music. But, when given the choice of two types of music you may not consider too often, which would you choose? Check one in each pair!

Would you rather listen to...

☐ Country   or   ☐ Classical?

Would you rather listen to...

☐ Hip Hop   or   ☐ Opera?

Would you rather listen to...

☐ Rock   or   ☐ Pop?

Would you rather listen to...

☐ Jazz   or   ☐ Techno?

Halloween Maze

Let's party! Follow the path from **Start** to **Finish** to guide the kids to the candy.

What's Your Future Career?

The future holds endless possibilities. You can do or be anything you want! Take this quiz to determine your future career.

Builder Designer Problem Solver

1. You're bored. What do you do?
- **A -** Gather bits and pieces of anything from around the house and build a robot.
- **B -** Grab my markers and draw the finest piece of graffiti known to man.
- **C -** Patrol the neighborhood to see if anyone needs my help with anything.

2. Your personal hero is:
- **A -** Frank Gehry
- **B -** Vincent Van Gogh
- **C -** Albert Einstein

3. Your prized possession is:
- **A -** My hammer
- **B -** My graphics programs
- **C -** My pretend badge

4. What's your dream vacation destination?
- **A -** Prague, to check out the architecture.
- **B -** Paris, to visit all the museums.
- **C -** New York City, to see the 9/11 Memorial.

5. What's your favorite type of TV show?
- **A -** Home improvement shows—I love to see what they build.
- **B -** Cartoons—they have the most awesome graphics.
- **C -** True crime, all the way.

Builder—Mostly As

You love to build stuff—you probably have all kinds of awesome tools. Your future career will be in architecture, where you can plan the building of structures or in actual construction, where you can be hands-on and do the building yourself.

Designer—Mostly Bs

You dig designing and drawing and love to appreciate others' creations, too. Your future career will be in graphic design or illustration. You'll design totally cool video games or cartoons or books and magazines.

Problem-Solver—Mostly Cs

You love to get to the bottom of a problem and to rescue people in trouble. Your future career will be in law enforcement as a police officer or a detective, or in firefighting. You'll be able to help people in need and solve crimes every day of your life.

Super Fan

Are you a super seeker? Put your eyes to the test and see if you can find 10 differences between the picture on the top and the one on the bottom.

Answer on page 293

Sudoku
THINK TANK

Dive into the think tank and try to decode this sudoku. Fill in the empty squares so that each row, column, and square contains the numbers 1–9 only once.

9					6	1		
	8				5	4		1
	1		8	4	2			
4		3	1			8		
				9				
	1				4	3		9
		3	5	6			1	
3		6	2				4	
		4	7					5

Design Your BREAKFAST OF CHAMPIONS

Ever mix a whole bunch of different cereals together? What did your concoction taste like? What would you have named it? Here's your chance to design your own brand of cereal!

ZOMBIE ATTACK!

Search, find, and circle these 10 things.

BANANA PEEL
BASKETBALL
BUTTON
COWBOY BOOT
EIGHT BALL
GOLF CLUB
NICKEL
SPOON
TACO
VIKING HELMET

Answer on page 293

Baseball
BASICS

Swing, batter, batter! It's time to learn the basics of baseball (and if you think you already know it all—it never hurts to brush up on your skills)!

THE BASICS

- A baseball game is played by two teams, each with nine players. The goal is to get enough hits and walks to round the bases and score more runs than your opponents.

THE EQUIPMENT

Mitt: A big leather glove that is used to catch the ball.
Baseball: A regulation baseball is three inches in diameter and has red stitching.
Bat: In professional baseball, players use wood bats (little league often uses metal bats).

THE FIELD

- The infield is the portion of the field closest to the bases.
- Anything beyond the bases is the outfield.
- Each base is ninety feet away from the next base.

DEFENSE - THE POSITIONS

Pitcher: Stands in the middle of the diamond and throws the ball to the batter.
Catcher: Squats behind the batter and catches any balls not hit (or foul balls in his territory). The catcher often tells the pitcher what kind of pitch to throw.
Infielders: The infielders are the first baseman, the second baseman, shortstop, and the third baseman.
Outfielders: The outfielders are the left fielder, the center fielder, and the right fielder.

THE GAME
- There are nine innings in professional baseball games.
- At the top of the inning, the home team fields and the visiting team is at bat. At the bottom of the inning, the opposite happens.
- Each team gets three outs per inning.

PLAYING OFFENSE
- The batting order cannot change during the game (but players can be substituted in).
- A batter gets three strikes per at bat.
- If the umpire calls four balls, the batter automatically advances to first base.
- A hit is technically when a player hits the balls and safely reaches a base without getting out or forcing another runner out.
- A homerun is a ball hit over the outfield walls, but within fair territory.

PLAYING DEFENSE
There are different ways the team on defense can get the other team out.
- Strikeouts (when a hitter misses three pitches)
- Force outs (when, after the ball is hit, the defensive player who caught or fielded the ball reaches a base before the runner)
- Fly outs (when a player hits the ball in the air and it's caught by a fielder before it hits the ground)
- Tag outs (when a runner is touched with the ball, or a glove with the ball in it)

Baseball Star

It's time to slide into home base! Can you find the two pictures that are exactly alike?

Answer on page 294

Write Your

What is the grossest thing you have ever done? What made it so memorable? Write a blog entry about it here!

SO GROSS!

Caption for your picture _____

_____
_____
_____
_____
_____
_____
_____
_____
_____
_____

post by_____ time _____

Let's Draw a
Velociraptor

On a separate piece of paper, follow these simple steps using a pencil and an eraser.

1 Lightly sketch an egg-shaped oval for the body. Next, using oval guidelines, very carefully create the upper and lower jaws, then connect them to the body. Then add the tail.

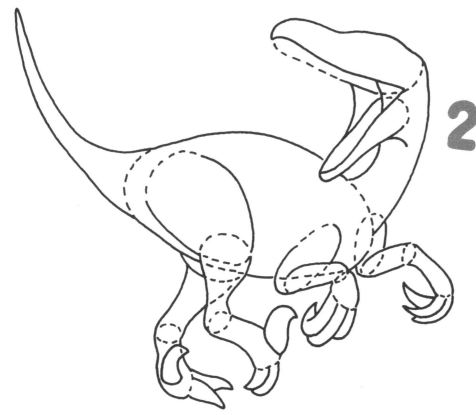

2 Using simple shapes, draw the arms, legs, and claws. Note the upturned claw on each foot.

3 Add the eye and teeth. Then refine all the shapes into a smooth outline of Velociraptor.

4 Add the final touches. Experts believe that Velociraptor hunted in packs, so you might want to draw several of them attacking a giant plant-eating dinosaur.

Making WORDS

Show your book smarts. Can you make 25 or more words from the following phrase?

ACTION FIGURE

Answer on page 294

Family Portrait

Are you a super seeker? Put your eyes to the test and see if you can find 10 differences between the picture on the top and the one on the bottom.

Answer on page 294

List Your

Travelin' Places

Think about all of the awesome places you've been in your life so far. Answer these questions and you'll remember all kinds of cool stuff about your travels!

 Where is the farthest you've ever traveled?

 What is the most exotic place you've ever been?

What is your favorite place to visit?

Ever traveled by plane? If so, where did you fly?

Which destination was your least favorite?

What is your favorite way to travel?

Decode-a-RIDDLE

Write the letter that comes THREE LETTERS AFTER each letter shown below to decode and solve the riddle.

T E X Q   H F K A

L C   B X O P   A L

Q O X F K P   E X S B ?

B K D F K B B O P

VIDEO GAMES

Find these things that have to do with video games in the word search below. Look up, down, backward, forward, and diagonally.

Arcade   Console   Gamer   Keyboard   Role playing

Computer   Controller   Joystick   Programmer   Television

```
N Q Q Y C C L K K C F R U R
J O F P R O C W O H T E C O
E X I R I I N N N B T T T L
U B S S T G T S G F V U H E
A R T S I R Y A O C U P S P
P V Y P O V M G B L E M M L
G O L L F E E B N S E O G A
J R L Z R W S L V T W C V Y
K E Y B O A R D E F W A K I
R A M U K W X U X T I R U N
T N A F C S Y I J L I C M G
F J U Y R S R P U A U A F I
T G O Q B N B F J B S D X K
P R E M M A R G O R P E B Y
```

Design Your Own
VIDEO GAME

You know how, when you're playing a video game, you think of a million ways you would re-do the game to make it even more awesome? Well, here's your chance to design your own video game!

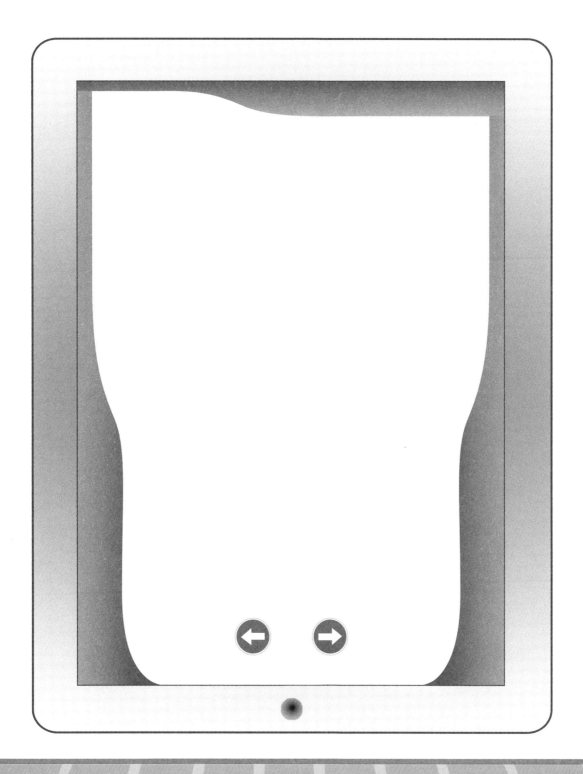

YUMMY BREAKFAST!

Use the clues about breakfast to complete this crossword puzzle.

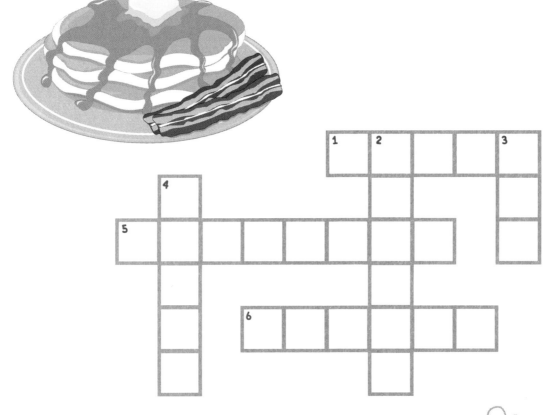

ACROSS
1. Cooked bread
5. Round, flat, and yummy
6. You usually pour milk over this

DOWN
2. Made with eggs and other ingredients mixed in
3. Some people drink this instead of coffee
4. A meat you eat with eggs

Answer on page 295

Basketball Maze

Follow the correct path through the maze to get the basketball to the hoop. What's the correct path, you ask? It's the one that is made up of basketballs only.

START ↓

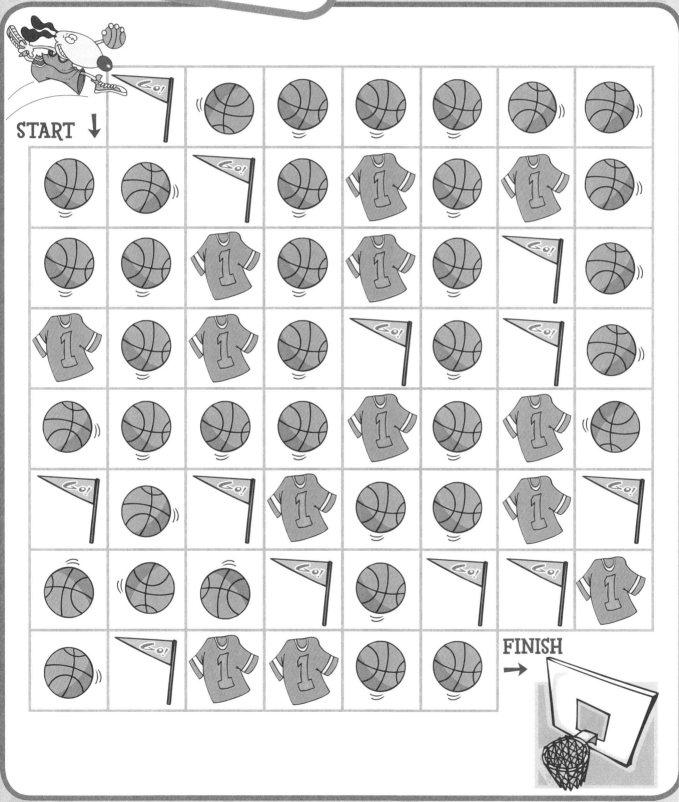

FINISH →

Skateboarding FACTS

Are you big into skateboarding, or is it something you've always wanted to try? Check out these fun skateboarding facts!

There are 18.5 million skateboarders in the world—74% of boarders are male.

Skateboarding started in California during the sixties as something for surfers to do when there wasn't a good swell in the ocean. The first skateboards looked a lot more like mini surfboards than the ones we know today, and skateboarding itself was called "sidewalk surfing."

Go Skateboarding Day was created in 2004 as a way for companies to make the public aware of the sport, and to inspire people to pick up a skateboard. Celebrate it every June 21!

In 1999, Tony Hawk became the first person to land a "900." The 900 is when you spin 900 degrees in midair—that's two and a half revolutions!

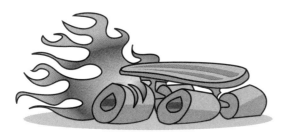

Super Skater

Let's skate! Can you find the two pictures that are exactly alike?

Let's Draw a Goblin

On a separate piece of paper, follow these simple steps using a pencil and an eraser.

1 Begin with an egg shape for the head and add on basic shapes for the body and legs. Add an area for the loincloth and boots.

2 Add arms, ears, and a hat. Next, add guidelines for the face.

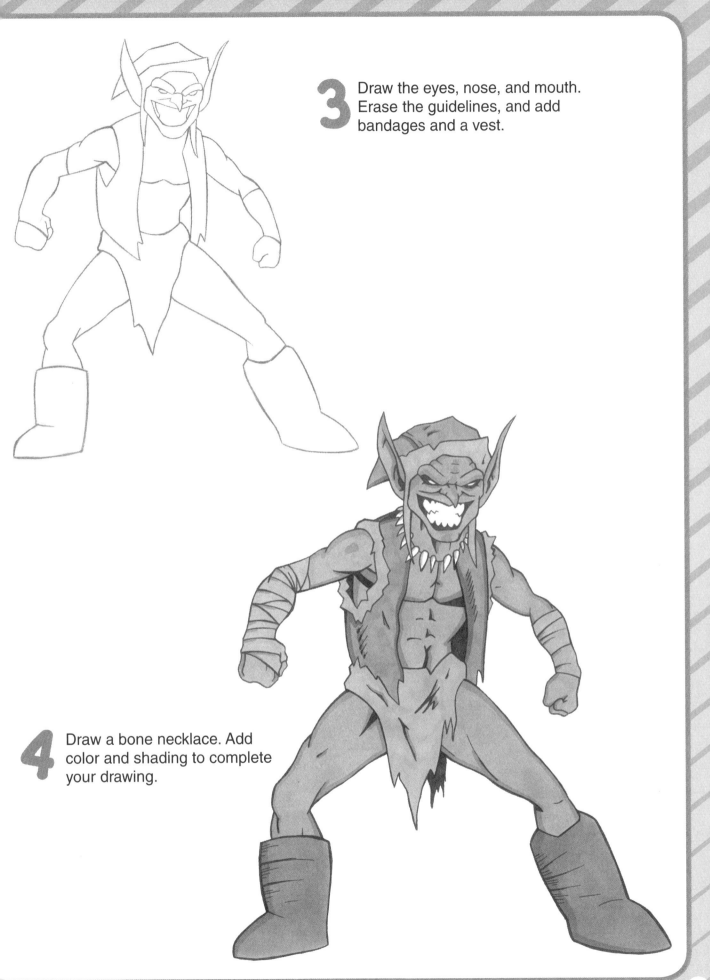

3 Draw the eyes, nose, and mouth. Erase the guidelines, and add bandages and a vest.

4 Draw a bone necklace. Add color and shading to complete your drawing.

CREATURE FEATURE

There is some serious mythical madness happening here! Find the names of these creatures in the word search below. Look up, down, backward, forward, and diagonally.

Bigfoot　　**Dragon**　　**Gnome**　　**Mermaid**　　**Ogre**

Centaur　　**Gargoyle**　　**Leprechaun**　　**Mummy**　　**Vampire**

```
N Y W C X S U R O A F B E S
W U Z Z N F U E G O R A L D
Y Z A Q W A R G A L S O Y E
F M W H T F B A A I Q J O U
Q B M N C V A M P I R E G E
N J E U I E D U D Q X K R S
M C Q Y M R R M G A B B A N
N E K H A V U P I V I E G K
J P R G C U D X E U G R F P
P Q O M E M O N G L F G C T
V N B V A X U E O T O O L C
O U E J Q I D Y X R O D Q W
W S R W T Q D S S P T F V Y
H F W Z D Z W J E U B E N M
```

Answer on page 296

Design Your Own
CREATE A CONVO

What is this kid saying to his Mom— and what is Mom thinking when she sees this seriously messed-up gift? Fill out the thought bubbles.

Design Your Own

ALIEN NATION

It's years into the future, and aliens have invaded the planet. They pick you to help them run the new planet. Time to get to work!

Name of New Planet

_____

Leaders of New Planet

_____
_____
_____
_____

Careers on New Planet

_____

I AM A TEACHER

Laws of New Planet

_____

_____

_____

School Subjects On New Planet

_____

_____

_____

Currency On New Planet

_____

Holidays of New Planet

_____

_____

_____

Bouncy Castle

Jump, jump, jump! Can you find the two pictures that are exactly alike?

Answer on page 296

Sudoku
BRILLIANT BRAINIAC

Put your brilliant brain on display and try to decode this sudoku. Fill in the empty squares so that each row, column, and square contains the numbers 1–9 only once.

							5	6
3			5	2				
9		5			1	2		
	3		1	5	4			
	7		8		3		1	
	6	7	9		8			
	2	1				9		5
			4	8				1
6	8							

Decode-a- RIDDLE

Use the code key below to decode and solve this riddle.

1=A	7=G	13=M	19=S	23=W
2=B	8=H	14=N	20=T	24=X
3=C	9=I	15=O	21=U	25=Y
4=D	10=J	16=P	22=V	26=Z
5=E	11=K	17=Q		
6=F	12=L	18=R		

$\overline{23}\ \overline{8}\ \overline{1}\ \overline{20}$ $\overline{19}\ \overline{8}\ \overline{15}\ \overline{21}\ \overline{12}\ \overline{4}$

$\overline{5}\ \overline{22}\ \overline{5}\ \overline{18}\ \overline{25}$ $\overline{19}\ \overline{12}\ \overline{15}\ \overline{16}\ \overline{16}\ \overline{25}$

$\overline{19}\ \overline{16}\ \overline{25}$ $\overline{8}\ \overline{1}\ \overline{22}\ \overline{5}$?

$\overline{1}\ \ \ \ \overline{12}\ \overline{9}\ \overline{3}\ \overline{5}\ \overline{14}\ \overline{19}\ \overline{5}$

$\overline{20}\ \overline{15}\ \ \ \ \overline{19}\ \overline{16}\ \overline{9}\ \overline{12}\ \overline{12}$

Ups and Downs

Solve this rebus puzzle to discover the name of something that has its ups and downs.

- ICE + ☐

- X + 👂 - E + D

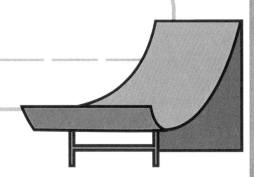

Snakes
FACTS

Slithery and slimy and oh-so-cool, snakes are your thing, huh? Want to learn more about them? Check out these fun facts!

Snakes are related to lizards.

Snakes turn "blue" before they shed. This change in color is due to a layer of fluid between the old and new skins, right before the shed of the old skin.

Venom can be poisonous to the heart, nerves, and DNA.

Two kinds of snakes, the grass snake and the spitting cobra, can fake death by flipping on their backs when threatened.

A snake's heart can slide 1 to 1 ½ times its length from its normal position, to allow the passage of swallowed prey.

Slithering Snake

This snake's slithering his way home. What do you think his humble abode is like? Draw a home for this slimy snake!

LIVING on the MOON

Fill in the blanks to complete this silly story about what it might be like to live on the moon. Pick a NOUN, ADJECTIVE, or VERB from the word bank to place in a corresponding blank, or think of your own wacky words!

Believe it or not, living on the moon is kind of _____ and
[ADJECTIVE]

it is totally not at all _____, like most people would think.
[ADJECTIVE]

The _____ who reside on the moon spend most of their
[NOUN]

days _____ in the hopes of being the first people to make
[VERB]

_____. The trip from Earth to the moon is very _____.
[NOUN]   ADJECTIVE]

Come on up and _____ some time!
[VERB]

WORD BANK

ADJECTIVES
delicious
insane   cool
creative   silly
dangerous   bent
intense   loud

NOUNS
pork chops   jars
guitars   brains
basketballs   under wear
hooks   stones
oatmeal

VERBS
whisper   hide
cram   crouch
chum   beep
lick   sleep
squirm

Making WORDS

Can you make 25 or more words from the following word?

EXPEDITION

Do You Have Good Manners?

Are you polite or are you a little bit too rude? To find out, read each statement, then put a check under "True" or "False." When you're done, go to the end of the quiz to see your results!

	TRUE	FALSE
1. I try not to be too loud.	◯	◯
2. I cover my mouth when I cough.	◯	◯
3. I use a tissue or handkerchief when I sneeze.	◯	◯
4. I don't litter.	◯	◯
5. I always knock on a door before I enter a room.	◯	◯
6. I try my best never to insult people.	◯	◯
7. I never interrupt people when they are talking.	◯	◯

	TRUE	FALSE

8. I always use silverware, not my hands, to eat.

9. Words like "sorry" and "thank you" are a big part of my vocabulary.

10. I always respect my elders.

11. I never use foul language.

POLITE DUDE

If you chose mostly "True" answers, you are a polite guy, which is a good thing. People tend to gravitate toward people who are polite to them, because they feel comfortable around them. Keep it up.

RUDE AND CRUDE

If you chose mostly "False" answers, you're a little on the rude side. Try to tone it down and adopt some better manners. You'll be surprised what a difference it makes.

Calculate an ERA

How To TIPS

Ever wonder how a baseball pitcher's ERA (or, Earned Run Average) is calculated? Here you go!

ERA Basics

1. Add up the total innings a pitcher pitched. For every out, you get one-third of an inning.

2. Now, add up the total number of earned runs given up. All the runs in an inning with no errors are earned runs. If there were errors in an inning, you have to go back and figure out how many runs would have scored had the fielding been perfect.

3. Next, multiply the earned runs by nine.

4. Divide that number by the number of total innings the pitcher pitched.

Write Your
BLOG

Do you have a secret that nobody knows about? What is it? And why do you keep it a secret? Write a blog entry about it here!

My Biggest Secret

Caption your picture _____

_____

_____

_____

_____

_____

_____

_____

_____

_____

post by_____ time_____

Let's Draw a
Treefolk

On a separate piece of paper, follow these simple steps using a pencil and an eraser.

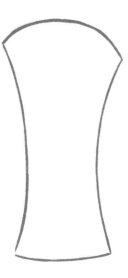

 Begin by drawing an apple core for the body.

2 Add an oval for the head. Next, draw the arms, hands, and legs.

3 Start to finalize the drawing by adding the face, hair, and root for toes. Add branches to the top of the head.

4 Draw the leaves, branch beard, and big shadow on the body. Finish the drawing with color and shading.

Werewolf Maze

Follow the path from **Start** to **Finish** to help the howling werewolf reach the moon.

FINISH

START →

Answer on page 297

WACKY WIZARDS

Search, find, and circle these 10 things.

BEARD

CAR

DALMATIAN

DUCK

FAIRY

FLYING PIG

HAMBURGERS (2)

ICE-CREAM SUNDAE

PIE

UNICORN

Design Your Own
AWESOME
CITY

You've just been assigned to the City Planning Commission. Draw in the rest of this city and add stuff to the buildings that are already there. What else does this city need? Who are the people who live there?

Would You Rather...

Which would you rather do?
Look at each pair of options. Think
about them and check the things you
would like best. Ask your friends, too!

Would you rather...

☐ Drink mud   or   ☐ Eat chalk?

Would you rather be able to...

☐ Sing   or   ☐ Dance?

Would you rather have...

☐ One big brother   or   ☐ One big sister?

Would you rather skip...

☐ Christmas   or   ☐ Your birthday?

Let's Draw a
Monster Truck

On a separate piece of paper, follow these simple steps using a pencil and an eraser.

1 This monster truck starts with one basic body shape and four huge tire shapes. It is important to draw through those tire shapes so they are correct.

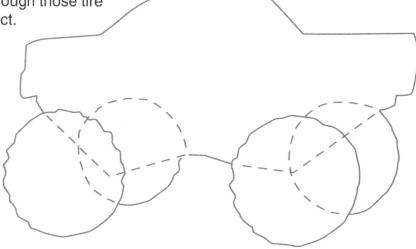

2 Establish the body by drawing the wheel wells, the truck bed, windows, and doors. Erase any unwanted lines to clean up the wheels and add rims.

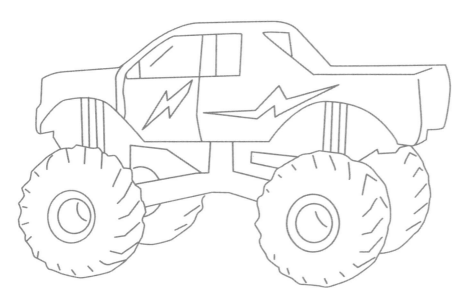

3 Use lines to show tire treads and the giant shocks. Show chassis and rim details and add some cool graphics on the side.

4 Use a bright red and yellow color combination and make sure you show plenty of highlights on the big treads! This monster truck looks like it can roll over anything!

Make Cool Knots!

How To TIPS

Like the scouts say, it's always good to be prepared. You never know when you'll be in a situation that will require you to tie up some complicated knots. Check out these three knots and how to tie them!

THE SQUARE KNOT

This knot is used to bind things or hold them together.

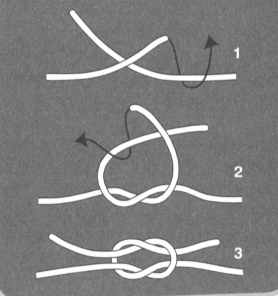

THE BOWLINE

This knot is used to make a loop and it is often used for rescue missions.

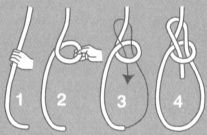

After the bowline has been formed, you must tighten it correctly like this:

Tightened correctly

Tightened incorrectly

TWO HALF HITCHES

This knot can be used to tie almost anything.

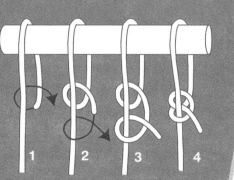

TYPES OF KNOTS

Find these things that have to do with knots in the word search below. Look up, down, backward, forward, and diagonally.

Bowline   **Figure eight**   **Loop**   **Reef knot**   **Slip knot**

Coil   **Half hitch**   **Overhand**   **Rope**   **Square knot**

```
F X E Q S H M Z V Z T E I H
T I X G Q I H Q E I N G A C
O Y G V U P L U A I F L U O
N B K U A T P O L J F E W B
K N L B R O O W O H A Z R M
P G R Q E E O N I P R U V Y
I P R Q K B E T K O B L O R
L L O P N S C I T F C I N K
S X P U O H Y A G P E E S M
M D E Z T D D N A H R E V O
D Q K I J T B W N W T W R Y
C I K Z H W O H F U X J C A
V X T R L T K P I H Q P P A
T H N L F W Y Z C O I L M Q
```

Answer on page 298

Baseball Fever

Are you a super seeker? Put your eyes to the test and see if you can find 10 differences between the picture on the top and the one on the bottom.

Answer on page 298

Making WORDS

Can you make 15 or more words of five or more letters from the following phrase?

HELICOPTER TRIP

Rock and Roll

It's time to rock and roll! Can you find the two pictures that are exactly alike?

Answer on page 298

• List Your

Music Mania

List all of your favorite songs, artists, bands, and more right here. While you're at it, crank up your MP3 player!

My favorite bands:

When I'm in a good mood, I listen to:

My favorite songs of all time:

When I'm in a bad mood, I listen to:

The best CDs of all time:

The most awesome videos:

Sudoku
SMART AS A WHIP

You're smart as a whip, so try to decode this sudoku. Fill in the empty squares so that each row, column, and square contains the numbers 1–9 only once.

5	4	6					7	
	9	6			7			
7			2			4		
5			4	7		6	3	
				1				
	1	2		9	8			4
		3			4			7
			7				9	6
	7						2	4

Answer on page 299

Mixed-up STORIES

The story below is listed in the wrong order. Write the numbers of the correct order in the spaces below.

After learning about coral reefs, Roberto asks his parents if he can take scuba diving lessons.
1

Roberto makes a scrapbook of pictures he took with a special underwater camera.
2

Roberto and his parents fly to the Bahamas to learn to scuba dive.
3

_____

_____

_____

_____

_____

_____

Roberto sees his favorite kind of fish, a parrotfish.
4

Roberto writes a report for science class and becomes interested in coral reefs.
5

Roberto and his parents get on a boat headed away from their hotel in the Bahamas.
6

Answer on page 299

Explorer Maze

Follow the correct path through the maze to get the shark to the map. What's the correct path, you ask? It's the one that is made up of blue fish only!

START

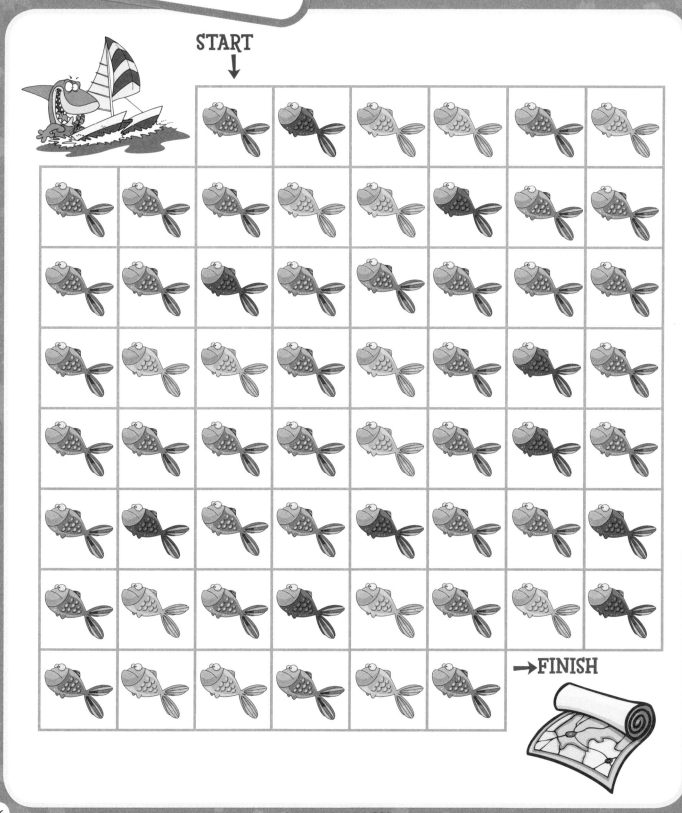

→ FINISH

Answer on page 299

Decode-a- RIDDLE

Use the code key below to decode and solve this riddle.

1=A 8=H 15=O 22=V
2=B 9=I 16=P 23=W
3=C 10=J 17=Q 24=X
4=D 11=K 18=R 25=Y
5=E 12=L 19=S 26=Z
6=F 13=M 20=T
7=G 14=N 21=U

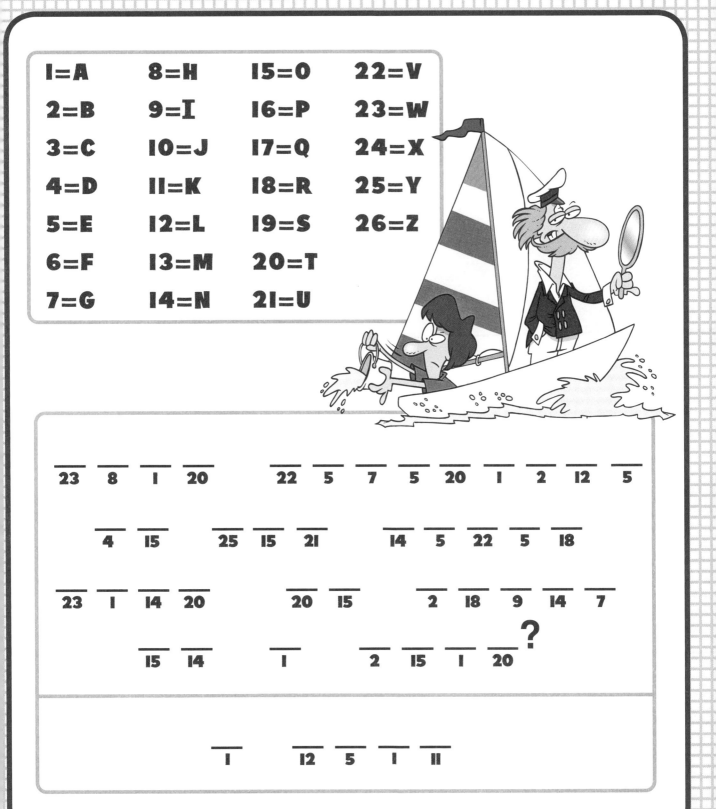

___ ___ ___ ___   ___ ___ ___ ___ ___ ___ ___ ___ ___
23 8   1   20   22 5   7   5   20 1   2   12 5

    ___ ___   ___ ___ ___   ___ ___ ___ ___ ___
    4   15   25 15 21   14 5   22 5   18

___ ___ ___ ___   ___ ___   ___ ___ ___ ___ ___
23 1   14 20   20 15   2   18 9   14 7

    ___ ___   ___   ___ ___ ___ ___?
    15 14   1   2   15 1   20

___   ___ ___ ___ ___
1   12 5   1   11

Read a Compass
How To
TIPS

Need some direction in your life? If you are ever lost or stranded, and happen to have a compass, you will need to know how to use it. Here's a step-by-step guide.

Compass Basics

1. Turn the compass until the North arrow on the face of the compass is lined up with the North side of the pointer. The compass is now aligned.

2. Now, look at the numbers. These are degrees, another way of measuring the compass direction.

3. Face any direction. Hold one of your hands out and place the compass flat in your palm. Point the arrow in the same direction you are facing.

4. Next, turn the dial on the compass so that the North-facing arrow is lined up with the pointer.

5. Read the degree mark that the index line goes across. That is your direction in degrees.

Use your compass know-how and create a cool map of your neighborhood.

SPORTS OF ALL SORTS

Play ball! Or, dive in! Whatever your sport of choice is, find the names of these sports in the word search. Look up, down, backward, forward, and diagonally.

Baseball **Football** **Hockey** **Softball** **Tennis**
Basketball **Golf** **Soccer** **Swimming** **Volleyball**

```
J B Q S S B F C H A S W L N
R V L U I C A L Q O O L Q S
K B L E B N M S F A A G I W
I N A R S X N T E B H H E I
O I B G J C B E T B U B M M
J F Y H P A U E T U A K E M
Y P E A L V K T R T F L B I
E I L L C S R E C C O S L N
K E L T A F O O T B A L L G
C B O B F Y K G Y N I A K Z
O M V L D O D I T I G X M D
H F O K F R T I W H D U Y D
Y G W O W C N M Q H O Y E M
V T C U W Z R N O M Q N F W
```

Answer on page 300

Wrestling FACTS

Most people know that wrestling is a professional sport, but did you know that the sport itself goes back a long, long time? Enhance your wrestling knowledge with these fun facts!

The word "wrestling" originated as a term for hand-to-hand combat in Old English. It dates back before 1100 A.D., and is one of the oldest words in the modern English language that still retains its original meaning!

Wrestling was a popular sport in ancient Greece, and is most associated with this era because it was the top sport of the early Olympic games. However, wrestling goes back 15,000 years— we know this because cave drawings in France show people wrestling!

Sumo is an ancient form of Japanese wrestling in which two opponents try to force each other outside of a ring. Sumo still exists today, but in the 1600s, most sumo wrestlers were unemployed samurai who needed a source of income. Even warriors need to work!

BEST WRESTLING

Fill in the blanks to complete this silly story about inventing your own signature wrestling move. Pick a NOUN, ADJECTIVE, or VERB from the word bank to place in a corresponding blank, or think of your own wacky words!

Forget about all the wrestling moves you've seen before—I've

come up with the most _____ move ever! In order to perform
[ADJECTIVE]

this super- _____ move, you have to _____ your opponent
[ADJECTIVE]   [VERB]

and then _____ and _____ the _____. If you try it and
[VERB]   [VERB]   [NOUN]

wind up in a _____, head to the doctor immediately!
[NOUN]

GRRRRR!!

WORD BANK

ADJECTIVES

tight
swell
beautiful
intricate
weird
wild
cold
blue
little

NOUNS

heap
pile
pretzel
bucket
fence
squirrel
tree
drawer
noggin

VERBS

slam
kick
lift
look
nap
run
sweat
burn
bend

NO SCHOOL TODAY!

Use the clues below to complete this crossword puzzle about days when you don't have school.

ACROSS
1. Season between Spring and Fall
2. Special type of "day" like Christmas or Easter
3. When you have a cold or toothache, you're _____.
4. When parents meet with teachers
5. Teachers go to these group events to discuss stuff.

DOWN
1. You do a lot of digging in these types of storms.

Answer on page 300

Let's Draw a
Stegosaurus

On a separate piece of paper, follow these simple steps using a pencil and an eraser.

1 Start by drawing your Stegosaurus by lightly sketching these basic shapes: first, a large oval, then two smaller ovals and a triangle.

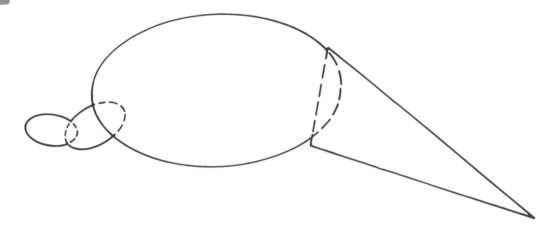

2 Draw some triangles on the tail and diamond-shaped plates on the back. Add ovals for the legs and feet.

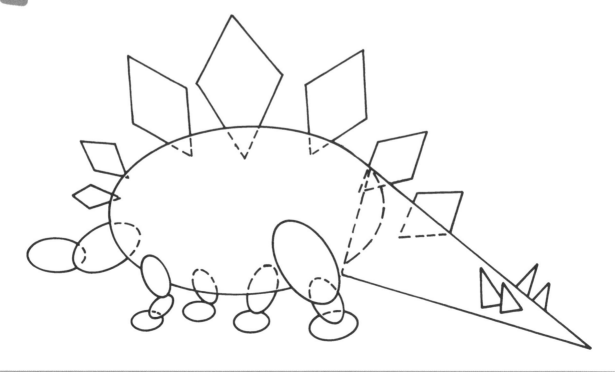

3 Take all your guidelines and blend them into this dinosaur's basic shape. Erase any unnecessary lines so that you have a clean line drawing of your Stegosaurus.

4 Put the finishing touches on your drawing. Add texture to the back plates and some spots to Stegosaurus's back.

Hockey TERMS

Grab your hockey stick and get ready to hit the ice! But, before you do, brush up on all of these important hockey terms. You'll go pro in no time at all!

Attacking Zone: The area of the ice that goes from the blue line to the end boards and belongs to the opposing team.

Backhand: Pass shot that is hit with the back of the stick's blade.

Blocker: A rectangular pad that the goalie wears on the hand he uses to hold his stick.

Boarding: Slamming, or checking, a player roughly into the boards. This is a penalty.

Boards: The walls surrounding the playing area of the ice.

Breakaway: When a player is in possession of the puck and there are no opposing players, except the goalie, between him and the goal.

Center: A player whose main area of play is the center of the ice.

Cherry Picking: This is when a player stays near the other team's goal waiting for someone to pass him the puck in order to make a breakaway shot.

Clipping: Hitting an opponent below the knees.

Face-off: This is how the game starts at the beginning of each period. Both teams line up across from each other and one player from each teams tries to get possession of the puck after it is dropped, by an official, between the teams.

Goal: When the puck goes totally into the goal frame, past the goal line, it is considered a goal.

Hat Trick: This is when a player scores three goals in a single game.

Hip Check: When a player uses his hip to bump an opponent.

Overtime: When, at the end of a regulation game, the score is tied, extra time is added. This is called overtime. The game is won by the first team to score a goal in overtime.

Penalty Box: This is the area a player sits in when a penalty is charged to him.

Power Play: When players are charged with penalties, and are in the penalty box, the other team has more players on the ice during that time. This is a power play.

Rebound: This is when the puck bounces off of the goalie, a player or the net after a shot.

Referee: This is the person in charge of officiating the game and making sure everyone is playing by the rules.

Saucer Pass: A saucer pass is when one player passes the puck, in the air and not on the ice, to another player.

Slap Shot: A very hard shot that is made when a player slaps his stick against the ice to launch the puck.

Wrist Shot: This is a shot taken with the open-faced part of the stick.

Zone: The three different areas of the ice, as divided by blue lines. The three zones are the attacking zone, neutral zone, and the defensive zone.

HOCKEY STUFF

Use the clues about hockey to solve the crossword puzzle.

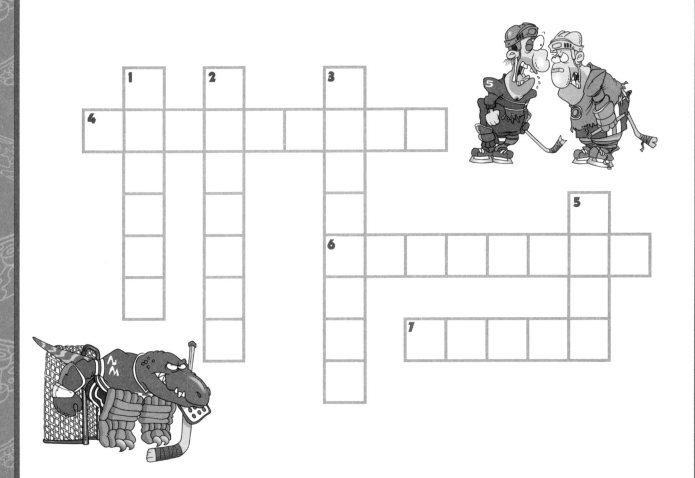

ACROSS
4. This happens when one team has more players on the ice than the other.
6. This is used to decide the winning team; players take turns trying to score.
7. To do this is to bump another player out of the way.

DOWN
1. This player tries to keep the other team from scoring.
2. A player gets this if he violates a rule.
3. A hard-hitting shot at the goal from a distance away
5. This is what all the players scramble to get.

Answer on page 300

Sudoku
SUPER STRENGTH

Try to decode this super tough sudoku. Fill in the empty squares so that each row, column, and square contains the numbers 1–9 only once.

		5					6	1
		3		6		2		5
			5				9	3
	3	1		9	8			2
7			4		5			6
			2	7		3	5	
	4				3			
3		7		8		1	2	4
2	9					6		

What's Your Color?

Did you know that color preference says a lot about you? What color best suits you and your personality? Take this quiz to determine your color.

Passionate   Calm   Mysterious

1. The word that best describes me is:
- **A** - Fun.
- **B** - Loyal.
- **C** - Secretive.

2. My favorite season is:
- **A** - Summer.
- **B** - Fall.
- **C** - Winter.

3. When on a team:
- **A** - I am just one of the guys.
- **B** - My plays make others look great.
- **C** - I like to be in charge.

4. Let's talk about fights:
- **A** - I start them.
- **B** - I mediate them.
- **C** - I end them.

5. Do you think you will ever get a tattoo?:
- **A** - Maybe.
- **B** - Never.
- **C** - Can't wait.

6. What kind of pet do you have?:
- **A** - Pit bull.
- **B** - Beagle.
- **C** - Saint Bernard.

Passionate—Mostly As

Your color is definitely red. You are passionate about stuff and go after whatever it is that you want at the moment.

Calm—Mostly Bs

Your signature color is blue, for sure. You are calm and peaceful and one of the most loyal guys out there!

Mysterious—Mostly Cs

Your signature color is purple, no doubt about it. You have an air of mystery about you and like to live on the edge and crave power.

BIRTHDAY PARTY

Search, find, and circle these 10 things.

BLUE CAKE

BUTTERFLY

DIAMOND

DUCK

EYEGLASSES

FISH

FORKS (3)

ICE-CREAM CONE

SNAKE

TEDDY BEAR

Answer on page 301

OUT OF THIS WORLD

There's a whole new world out there in outer space! Find the names of these planets and their galaxy in the word search below. Look up, down, backward, forward, and diagonally.

Earth	Mars	Milky Way	Pluto	Uranus
Jupiter	Mercury	Neptune	Saturn	Venus

```
M N E B Y L M M S W O T G S
N I R W C O W E U F B V U S
A X L U S C X R N J H N Z J
X X I K T Y Y C A G E C U J
R A C U Y A N U R V Q P M H
E A R T H W S R U I I T R P
N Q H Y A Y A Y F T W L R K
E N U T P E N Y E X T X S P
J J N O M I V R N E R V R B
A C D W Q D P O B X C O A B
Q K A C Y J U L B H R U M Q
R Y U L Z F V X U B U P G H
P W L U C X D U G T I Q I U
K L Z V M V Z M S T O N A Y
```

SNOW Day

Are you a super seeker? Put your eyes to the test and see if you can find 10 differences between the picture on the top and the one on the bottom.

Answer on page 301

Out on the Lake

Solve this rebus puzzle to discover a leisurely pastime on a lake.

S +

- M + - K

_ _ _ _ _ _ _ _ _

List Your Lucky Lottery

Imagine winning a billion dollars in the lottery. What would you do with all that dough? Make your wish list here, so you'll be prepared when you strike it rich!

 The first thing I would buy is:

  Charities I'd donate to:

 I would buy my parents:

 I would hire a:

 Friends I'd give some cash to:

Dart FACTS

People all around the world play darts—and it's been around for a super long time. Want to learn more this cool sport? Check out these awesome dart facts.

The Pilgrims played darts on the Mayflower! They brought the game with them to America, along with another game still played today—horseshoes.

The first version of a dart was likely just an arrow, used with either a bow or crossbow, cut down to a smaller size. The first darts made specifically for the game of darts were produced in France and were decorated with turkey feathers.

Before World War I, dartboards were made from blocks of wood, rather than the cork or fiber used today. This meant that you had to soak the dartboard each night to "heal" the holes made by the darts—otherwise you wouldn't be able to play!

Let's Draw a
Gargoyle

On a separate piece of paper, follow these simple steps using a pencil and an eraser.

1 Draw a large oval for the head, arms, and legs. Add the legs, as shown.

2 Next, lightly sketch the head and arms, as shown.

3 Add the wings, and details to the face and legs. Erase any unwanted guidelines.

4 You are now ready to draw the teeth. Finally, add color and shadowing.

Decode-a- RIDDLE

Use the code key below to decode and solve this riddle.

1=A	7=G	13=M	19=S	22=V
2=B	8=H	14=N	20=T	23=W
3=C	9=I	15=O	21=U	24=X
4=D	10=J	16=P		25=Y
5=E	11=K	17=Q		26=Z
6=F	12=L	18=R		

GARAGE SALE

__ __ __ __   __ __   __ __ __
23 8 1 20   4 15   25 15 21

__ __   __ __ __ __   __ __
4 15   23 9 20 8   1 14

__ __ __   __ __ __ __ ?
15 12 4   2 9 11 5

__ __ __
25 15 21

__ __ - __ __ __ __ __ __ __
18 5   3 25 3 12 5 9 20

Ice-Cream Truck

Are you a super seeker? Put your eyes to the test and see if you can find 10 differences between the picture on the top and the one on the bottom.

Puppy Maze

Follow the correct path through the maze to get the dog to the bone. What's the correct path, you ask? It's the one that is made up of paw prints only!

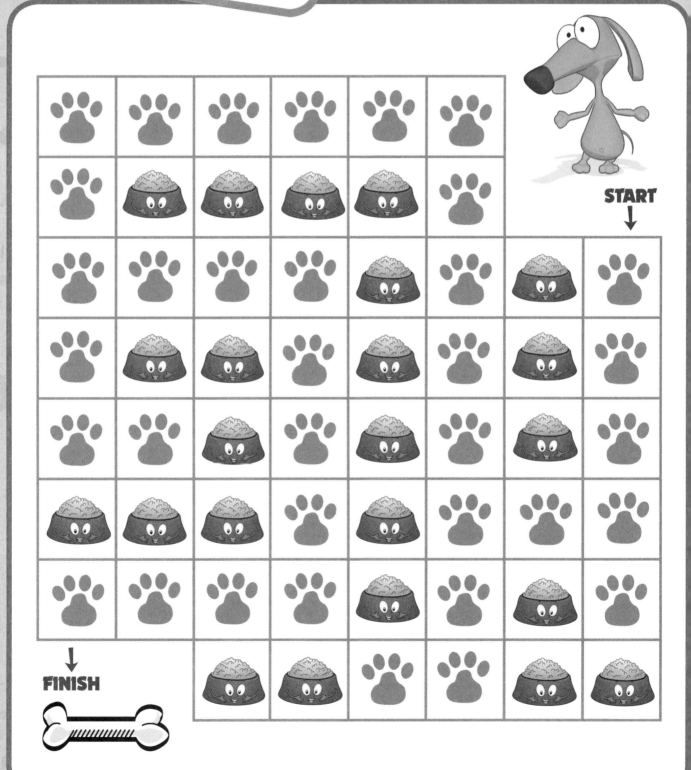

START

FINISH

Answer on page 302

Making WORDS

Use your travel smarts. Can you make 25 or more words from the following word?

GLOBETROTTER

Answer on page 302

GO, GO, GO

Rev up your engine and find the names of these vehicles in the word search below. Look up, down, backward, forward, and diagonally.

Airplane   **Car**   **Monster truck**   **Rickshaw**   **Wagon**

Big rig   **Helicopter**   **Motorcycle**   **Taxi**   **Yacht**

```
E W G G V G P C V H B M J W
U N I D I U B C E H B O G A
S D A R K N F L C X M N J H
T O G L U T I A T H H S G S
P I H U P C M A Z E F T P K
B H C H O R Y A C H T E E C
D A U P W V I P Z D N R O I
R A T K R A O A U Y T T N R
R E K K V N G Z P S N R X E
R E L C Y C R O T O M U C H
G M E B Y K U N N Z J C S T
I A C I L C A N H P L K T A
N Q P N N N F C Y M E C O X
S J A G Q E J M K N I R U I
```

Answer on page 303

CAR PARTS

Use the clues about car parts to complete this crossword puzzle.

ACROSS
2. Storage space in back
4. Helps the driver see around the car
7. Plays music
9. The "shoes" of the car
10. Needed for driving at night

DOWN
1. The "heart" of the car
3. Makes the car stop
5. Keeps everyone in the car safe
6. Lets other drivers know where you are
8. Pops out if there's an accident

Answer on page 303

Dinosaur Maze

It's a prehistoric flashback! Follow the path from **Start** to **Finish** to guide the baby dinosaur to its mother.

Answer on page 303

Write Your

What do you want to be when you grow up? How do you plan on making it happen? Write a blog entry about it here!

When I Grow Up!

Caption your picture _____

_____

_____

_____

_____

_____

_____

_____

_____

_____

_____

post by _____ time _____

GOLF

Grab your club and find these golf terms in the word search below. Look up, down, backward, forward, and diagonally.

Ball	Club	Green	Par	Swing
Birdie	Course	Iron	Score	Wood

```
F R P X A E K O C P K G G
D F J C E L X W O W A P J
L S T E S W N R U N C R B
A K Z L L A B K R P A X G
I P L A N V J V S I M C C
F A Y E B Q W W E N T K O
V C E U N H W O F O I S S
D R L E B O Z L U J J O C
G C L W O I I R O N B X O
M F V D V V R R B X G A R
C O G C E M A D S E H N E
B C R P W X C B I P J G C
T J L S W I N G G E B H Y
```

Answer on page 303

Cool Tree House

Are you a super seeker? Put your eyes to the test and see if you can find 10 differences between the picture on the top and the one on the bottom.

Answer on page 304

Are You Cut Out for Camping?

Camping seems like so much fun! Are you cut out for this kind of outdoor adventure? To find out, read each statement, then put a check under "True" or "False." When you're done, go to the end of the quiz to see your results!

	TRUE	FALSE
1. If I could, I would be outdoors all day long.	◯	◯
2. I can build a fire.	◯	◯
3. Insects don't bother me.	◯	◯
4. I don't need a comfy bed to sleep well.	◯	◯
5. I can go days without showering.	◯	◯
6. I don't need gourmet meals.	◯	◯
7. Extreme temperatures don't affect me.	◯	◯

	TRUE	FALSE
8. I have a good sense of direction.	◯	◯
9. I don't need to watch TV.	◯	◯
10. I know the difference between poison ivy and poison oak.	◯	◯
11. I know how to find the North Star.	◯	◯

EXPERT CAMPER

If you chose mostly "True" answers, you are a camper at heart. Sleeping in a tent, even if it's raining, wouldn't faze you in the least. You have what it takes to be an expert camper!

CAMPING ROOKIE

If you chose mostly "False" answers, you might want to rethink that camping trip. You like creature comforts, and camping means roughing it. But, give it a try, anyway—you never know!.

Create Your OWN LIST

Sure, girls aren't all that bad, but it's really cool to be a boy. What makes being a boy so cool? List all the reasons you can think of in the blanks.

It's Great Being a Boy Because:

_____   _____

_____   _____

_____   _____

_____   _____

_____   _____

_____   _____

_____   _____

Mixed-up STORIES

The story below is listed in the wrong order. Write the numbers of the correct order in the spaces below.

1. Mark cooks some food in a special pot that hangs over his campfire.

2. Mark sets up his tent on the flattest spot.

3. Mark pours water over his campfire and stirs the ashes to make sure it is out.

4. Mark sweeps away any sticks and rocks so that his tent can lie flat.

5. Mark makes sure all his food is sealed up so animals don't bother him as he sleeps.

6. Mark gathers water to keep near his campfire, and small sticks to get the fire started.

__ __ __ __ __ __

Answer on page 304

Identify Animal Tracks

How To TIPS

Do you know the difference between a dog track and a coyote track? It's good info to have—if you want to stay safe!

Animal Tracks Guide

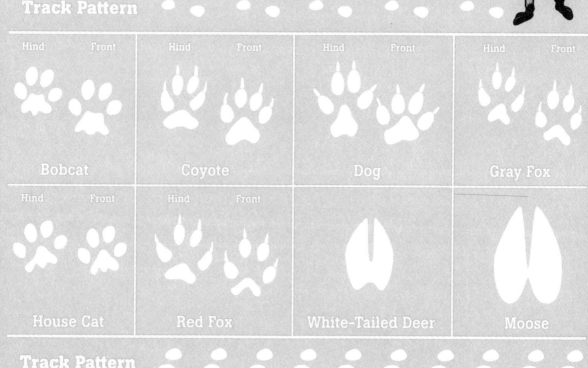

Track Pattern

Hind	Front
	Bobcat

Hind	Front
	Coyote

Hind	Front
	Dog

Hind	Front
	Gray Fox

Hind	Front
	House Cat

Hind	Front
	Red Fox

White-Tailed Deer

Moose

Track Pattern

Hind	Front
	Otter

Hind	Front
	Fisher

Hind	Front
	Weasel

Track Pattern

Raccoon	Stripped Skunk	Porcupine	Beaver
Hind / Front	Hind / Front	Hind / Front	Hind / Front

Black Bear	Opossum	Woodchuck	Muskrat
Hind / Front	Hind / Front	Hind / Front	Hind / Front

Track Pattern

Snowshoe Hare	Cottontail Rabbit	Gray Squirrel	White-Footed Mouse
Hind / Front	Hind / Front	Hind / Front	Hind / Front

MISCELLANOUS

Turkey	Crow	Ruffed Grouse

"B" THERE OR "B" SQUARE

Who knew there were so many countries that begin with the letter "B?" Find the names of these countries in the word search below. Look up, down, backward, forward, and diagonally.

Bahamas	**Bangladesh**	**Belgium**	**Bolivia**	**Brazil**
Bali	**Barbados**	**Bermuda**	**Bosnia**	**Bulgaria**

```
Q H C L Z T B U A F L I B G
M Q S X P A R I T R Y W O V
W N X E H O R F Y P A U L R
B Y G A D A U O L Z W S I C
J N M J G A G B I I R O V J
U A A L Z T L H A Z Z D I Y
S B U L B E L G I U M A A T
Q B E X U V X S N Y A B R T
C C V R Q Q F V Z A W R A B
Z Z Z S M F S L I M B A A P
B B T R H U A I N S O B I E
M U Q O E H D O N I U J L Q
R H P W I J L A H Q C N A M
Z K Y T Y N N C S C K V B R
```

Answer on page 304

SOUVENIRS

Use the clues about different kinds of souvenirs to complete this crossword puzzle.

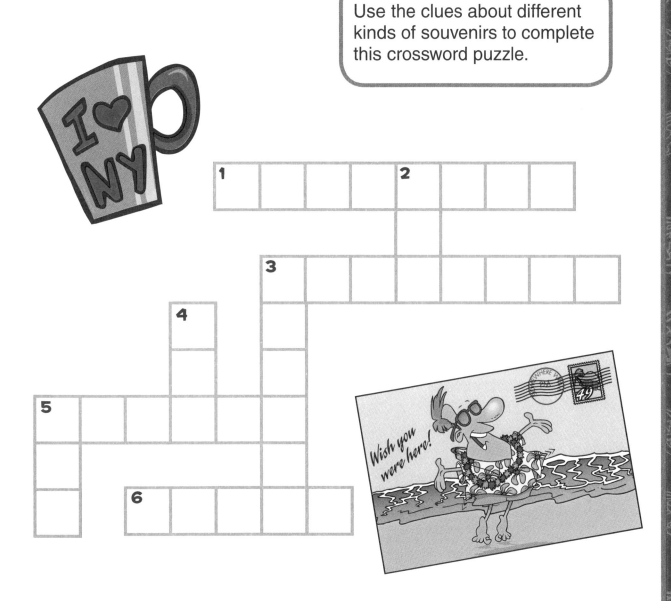

ACROSS
1. Dangles from a ring
3. Send this to a friend
5. Sticks to the fridge
6. Pull this over your head to show others where you've visited

DOWN
2. Goes on top of your head
3. Hang this on your wall
4. Be careful not to poke your finger with this!
5. Sip something from this

Answer on page 304

RAD ROBOT

Fill in the blanks to complete this silly story about what it might be like have a robot. Pick a NOUN, ADJECTIVE, or VERB from the word bank to place in a corresponding blank, or think of your own wacky words!

I built the most _____ robot in my basement last week.
[ADJECTIVE]

He is made of my _____ and _____
[NOUN]   [NOUN]

and he is _____. My favorite thing he does is when
[ADJECTIVE]

he _____s. But it's also pretty funny to see him
[VERB]

_____ my _____. Even my parents like him!
[VERB]   [NOUN]

I can't wait to _____ him to all my _____s.
[VERB]   [NOUN]

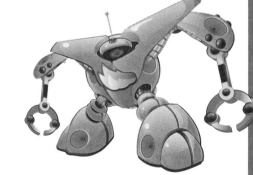

WORD BANK

ADJECTIVES	NOUNS	VERBS
warm	friend	bedroom	clean	shine
awesome smart	nose	laundry	cook	sip
pink stinky	book	mac and	sniffle	squeal
tall strong	poster	cheese	knock	burn
round squiggly	laptop	lollipop	twirl	

Rebus RUCKUS

Solve this rebus puzzle to discover the name of something that you hear around a stable.

-W +D +

-CAN +

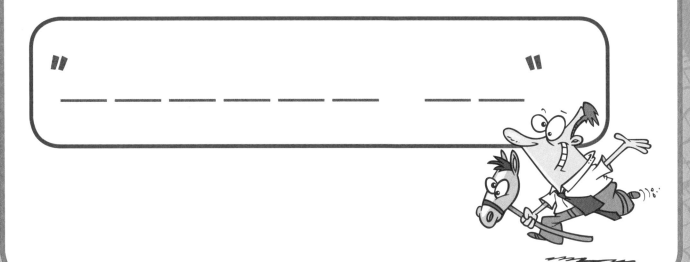

" _ _ _ _ _ _ _ _ _ _ _ _ _ _ _ _ _ _ _ "

Sudoku
PERFECT SKILLS

Show off your skills and try to decode this sudoku. Fill in the empty squares so that each row, column, and square contains the numbers 1–9 only once.

		9		1		2		7
8			2	6		1	9	
1	4		9					8
		4					6	
	9		3		1		8	
	1			8				2
7		5			4	8	1	9
	6			5	2			3
4		8		9		5		

Answer on page 305

Would You Rather...

Which would you rather do?
Look at each pair of options. Think about them and check the things you would like best. Ask your friends, too!

Would you rather give up...

☐ Your bike   or   ☐ Your computer?

Would you rather dye your...

☐ Hair blue   or   ☐ Hair pink?

Would you rather have...

☐ Candy   or   ☐ Ice cream?

Would you rather be...

☐ A dog   or   ☐ A cat?

Yo-Yo Tricks
How To
TIPS

A yo-yo trick, when done right, will impress your pals (and maybe that girl you have a crush on)! Here are some cool yo-yo tricks for you to try.

GRAVITY PULL

- Put the string around your middle finger.
- Your palm should be facing up.
- Throw the yo-yo down and lift your arm up, like you are making a muscle.
- When the yo-yo hits the bottom of the string, turn your palm down.
- Tug the yo-yo back up into your hand.

FORWARD PASS

- Put your hand behind your back, palm up.
- Release the yo-yo and bring your hand forward quickly.
- The yo-yo will go out in front of you.
- Pull it back to your hand and catch it.

THE SLEEPER

- Hold your yo-yo hand out with your palm and string facing up.
- Whip the yo-yo sharply toward the ground, like you're throwing a fastball.
- Have the yo-yo stay down—spinning—at the end of the string. While the yo-yo is spinning, turn your yo-yo hand over, palm facing down.
- You're doing it right if the yo-yo spins at the end of the string for a few seconds. Finally, give the string a jerk and the yo-yo should return to your hand.

THE WIND-UP

- Start with the yo-yo on the ground, still, not spinning.
- Pull it up as fast as you can.

LOOP THE LOOP

- Begin by throwing a forward pass.
- But, as the yo-yo comes back, do not catch it.
- Instead, turn your wrist and flick it back out.

ALL ABOUT YO-YOS!

Use the clues about yo-yos to complete this crossword puzzle.

ACROSS

3. A move where your yo-yo "walks" on the ground; 3 words

4. A move where you start with the yo-yo on the ground; 2 words

5. A move where you let the yo-yo hang before flicking it back up; 2 words

6. A move where you flick the yo-yo down and let it hang and spin

DOWN

1. A move where you don't catch the yo-yo and let it fling around; 3 words

2. A move where you release the yo-yo behind you, then pull it forward; 2 words

Answer on page 305

Ahoy, Matey!

Yo ho ho! Can you find the two pictures that are exactly alike?

Answer on page 305

Darts Maze

Follow the path from **Start** to **Finish** to guide the dart thrower to the bull's eye.

Answer on page 306

Mixed-up

STORIES

The story below is listed in the wrong order. Write the numbers of the correct order in the spaces below.

1. A family listens to a tour guide talk about ancient ruins.

2. A family gets on a bus and takes their seats.

3. A family asks a tour guide to take their picture so they can always remember their trip.

4. A family wakes up in their hotel.

5. A tour guide asks if anyone has any questions.

6. A family arrives at the site of some famous ruins.

— — — — — —

Answer on page 306

Create Your
ADVENTURE LIST

The world is a big, cool, interesting place. You could spend your whole life traveling and still not see the whole world. What are your dream destinations? List them!

Places 1 Want To Travel To:

_____   _____
_____   _____
_____   _____
_____   _____
_____   _____
_____   _____
_____   _____
_____   _____
_____   _____

TRUCKIN' AROUND

Search, find, and circle these 10 things.

ALLIGATOR
BASEBALL CAPS (3)
BASKETBALL
FISHBOWL
MONKEY
SET OF GOLF CLUBS
SKATEBOARD
SLIDE
SOCCER BALL
TRUMPET

Answer on page 306

Let's Draw a

Porsche Boxster

On a separate piece of paper, follow these simple steps using a pencil and an eraser.

1 Begin by drawing the body car, canopy, and tires. Use guidelines to keep shapes accurate.

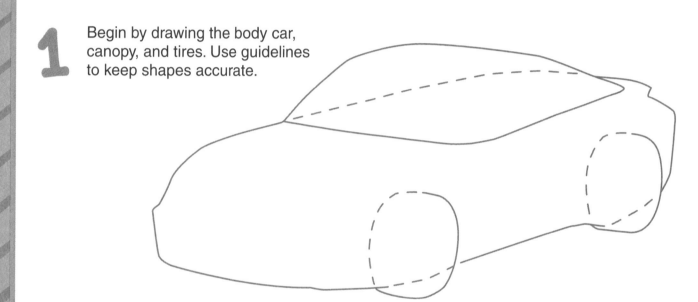

2 Erase the guideline. Next, draw the wheel wells, door, windows, and front bumper area. Add the front lights.

3 Draw interior details, glass door handle, and mirrors. Add hood detail and rims.

4 A yellow base with light and dark shadowing and black around the lights looks great. Add the black interior color with some gray accents, and head out to the highway.

ALL-STAR HOCKEY

Grab your hockey stick and find these hockey terms in the word search below. Look up, down, backward, forward, and diagonally.

Assist   **Goalie**   **Overtime**   **Pass**   **Puck**

Breakaway   **Interference**   **Pad**   **Penalty**   **Rebound**

```
B L O B I B N C M W M D S O
V P J E I X U C M K C U P P
E C N E R E F R E T N I L L
J P A S S Z W B U F E K G J
F H K G Z T P M Q Z P T R V
E Q A K Y A W A K A E R B E
K M A W D W B T D F B Q F Q
L Z I A R E B O U N D A L T
V B G T S N Y T L A N E P A
V R T O R S D C K A E W W Y
X R H Q A E I V S I C L J D
H I Z P F L V S X Q D D D V Q
L A R M F N I O T D D J S Z
W B M F E L S E U P N F M H
```

Fright Night

Are you a super seeker? Put your eyes to the test and see if you can find 10 differences between the picture on the top and the one on the bottom.

Answer on page 307

Build a Blanket Fort!
How To TIPS

This is a super-fun thing to do when you have your friends over. You'll have hours of fun in a blanket fort! Be sure to ask an adult for help and supervision.

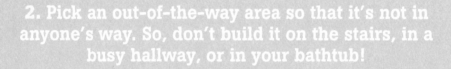

Blanket Fort Basics

1. It's always a good idea to ask your parents for permission first.

2. Pick an out-of-the-way area so that it's not in anyone's way. So, don't build it on the stairs, in a busy hallway, or in your bathtub!

3. Don't use items that somebody in the house might need.

4. Grab a few chairs and some sheets and/or blankets. If there are no chairs available, you could use the back of a couch or other furniture like that. It has to be a place that will hold your blanket well.

5. If you use chairs, situate them in a wide circle. If they are too close together, your fort could come crashing down.

6. Use safety pins to connect the sheets and blankets together. Be sure to ask an adult for help.

7. Drape the sheets and blankets over the top of the couches. Use clips or clothespins to keep the blankets on.

8. Leave an opening on the side of your fort for a door.

9. Leave an opening at the front and back of your fort for an entrance and an exit.

10. Place heavy objects along the edges of the sheets and blankets to hold them in place.

11. Pillows are good to use for walls or seats. Add a blanket and a few pillows inside to sit on.

What Animal Are You Most Like?

There are all sorts of personalities, and some people's traits can be compared to those of animals. Take this quiz to find out what kind of animal you're like.

Tiger   Golden Retriever   Turtle

1. You argue with your dad. You:
- **A -** Go nuts and throw stuff.
- **B -** Sulk for a while. Then talk it out.
- **C -** Hide for a while, then never bring it up again.

2. Your sport of choice is:
- **A -** Wrestling.
- **B -** Baseball.
- **C -** Golf.

3. Your favorite music is:
- **A -** Heavy Metal.
- **B -** Top 40.
- **C -** Jazz.

4. Your friends:
- **A -** Are sort of scared of you.
- **B -** Love hanging out with you.
- **C -** You don't have many friends.

5. Your favorite color is:
- **A -** Black.
- **B -** Blue.
- **C -** White.

6. In school, your favorite subject is:
- **A -** Math.
- **B -** Gym.
- **C -** Science.

Tiger—Mostly As

You are most like a tiger. You can be ferocious and tend to pounce on unsuspecting victims. Keep your fierceness, but tone it down a bit.

Golden Retriever—Mostly Bs

You are most like a golden retriever. You are loyal and loved and enjoy hanging out with your friends and doing guy stuff.

Turtle—Mostly As

You are most like a turtle. You are solitary and keep to yourself. It's okay to come out of your shell once in while!

TYPES OF SPIDERS

Use the clues about spiders to complete this crossword puzzle.

ACROSS
4. Very poisonous; 2 words
5. Named for its sphere-shaped web; 2 words
6. _____ spider; named after a fierce canine

DOWN
1. Named for the length of its limbs; 3 words
2. This type is sometimes a pet
3. Named for what it eats; 2 words (Hint: "It's a _____, it's a plane!")

Answer on page 307

Spider FACTS

Sure, they are spooky, creepy, and sometimes scary. But, spiders are do-gooders, too! Check out all of these cool spider facts!

Spiders are members of the arachnid family.

Most spiders use their fangs to inject the insect they are going to eat with venom. The venom will either instantly kill the prey or paralyze it. The spider then sprays digestive juices onto the solid tissue of the prey, which dissolves the tissue so that the spider can eat it.

Each year, on average, one person in the United States and three people in Europe die from spider bites.

Spiders can actually be pretty useful to humans. Spiders eat mosquitoes, which carry disease.

VIDEO DREAM

Fill in the blanks to complete this silly story about what it might be like to have a dream about living in your favorite video game. Pick a NOUN, ADJECTIVE, or VERB from the word bank to place in a corresponding blank, or think of your own wacky words!

You'll never believe this, but I had a dream that I was a part of my

favorite video game! It was the most _____ dream ever. I wore a
[ADJECTIVE]

_____ _____ and had a _____ as a weapon.
[ADJECTIVE]   [NOUN]   [NOUN]

Everyone around me was _____ and I had to _____ just
[ADJECTIVE]   [VERB]

to stay alive. I was never so _____ to wake up in my entire life!
[ADJECTIVE]

I can't wait to _____ again and go on another _____!
[VERB]   [NOUN]

WORD BANK

ADJECTIVES

sweet	sick
sour	strange
large	spicy
striped	quiet
red	

NOUNS

violin	engine
golf ball	umbrella
puck	salt
wig	strawberry
fork	

VERBS

shout	sweep
build	bounce
burp	walk
swallow	
yodel	

Awesome Astronaut

Watch out for the craters on the moon! Can you find the two pictures that are exactly alike?

ZOO CREW

The zoo is home to tons of super cool creatures! Find the names of these zoo animals in the word search below. Look up, down, backward, forward, and diagonally.

Alligator   **Orangutan**

Chimpanzee   **Polar bear**

Elephant   **Rhinoceros**

Giraffe   **Tiger**

Lion   **Zebra**

```
J T U E A C C H S L P P M K
Z F N R D F I F G A O B Z J
L O B A J Y V G C M L H Z U
C E Z I H P L Y T L A E X G
Z H O E S P F I O R R F C J
R H I N O C E R O S B F Z M
P G J M I H A L U N E A G K
C N C D P N K L E V A R N Q
V X C T G A W O X L R I C N
O B M U S C N I H L L G X Z
Q Q T I B M Y Z H T I G E R
X A E L A A D X E B E E M D
N K G K M L B C D E M J G S
V R O T A G I L L A E Q M F
```

Answer on page 307

Sudoku
PUZZLE POWER

Got lots of brain power? Then try to decode this sudoku. Fill in the empty squares so that each row, column, and square contains the numbers 1–9 only once.

		3	6	7				9
6	8							1
		9			1			8
		4			6	8		7
			8		2			
8		6	3			9		
9			1			5		
5							7	4
2				5	3	1		

Design Your Own
TV SHOW

Think about your favorite TV shows. Wouldn't it be cool if the best characters from each show crossed over? Here's your chance to create a TV show!

TV FACTS

Are you a TV nut or just a casual viewer? Improve your knowledge of TV with these fun facts!

The world's oldest TV station started up in 1928. But the broadcasts weren't anything like we see today. Because engineers were still testing the technology, the station only "played" images of a stuffed cat spinning on a turntable for two years!

Think reality TV is a new thing? It's existed since the 1940s in the form of prank shows and talent searches.

The "laugh track" is the audience laughter you can hear during most sitcoms. It's totally fake! Specialized engineers spend hours editing together a laugh track, and can even choose the volume, gender, and quality of the laughs!

Blast Off Maze

Follow the correct path through the maze to get the astronaut to Mars. What's the correct path, you ask? It's the one that is made up of rockets only!

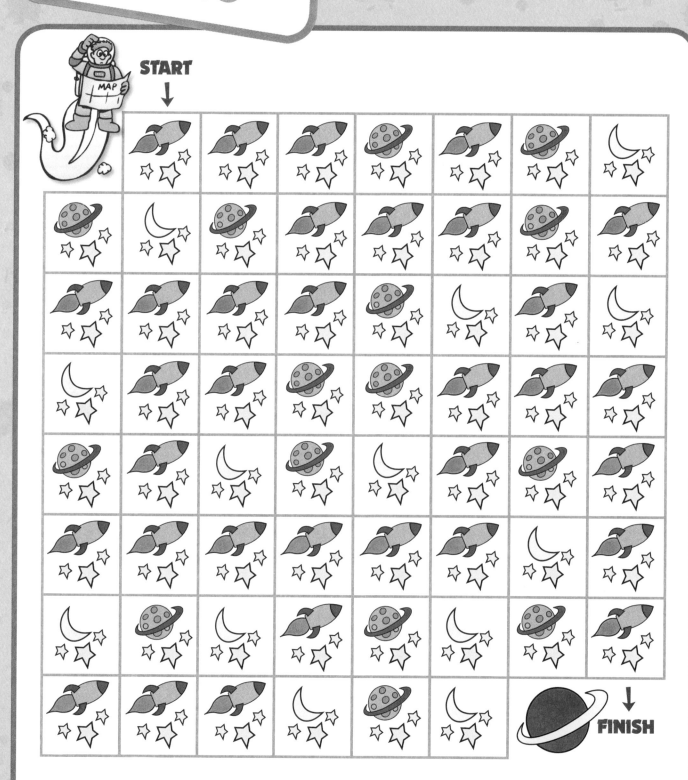

START

FINISH

Answer on page 308

Build It Up!

Solve this rebus puzzle to discover the name of a site where buildings are made.

 **- W + N +**

- OP + R + ⬆ **- P + C +**

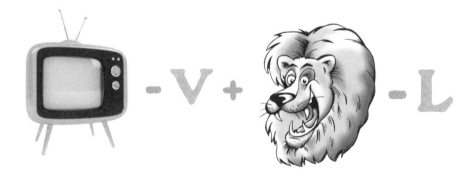 **- L**

_ _ _ _ _ _ _ _ _ _ _ _ _ _ _

Football TERMS

Before you grab the old pigskin or settle in to watch the game, make sure you know your stuff. Here are some important football terms and their meanings.

Backfield: This is the area of the field behind the line of scrimmage.

Blitz: This is a defensive move where the linebackers (who usually stay behind the line of scrimmage) rush into the other team's backfield.

Complete Pass: When a player passes the ball to a teammate, who catches it in the air, it is considered a complete pass.

Down: A down is a unit of the game that starts with a snap or a free kick, and ends when the ball becomes dead (if it is dropped, etc.). There are four downs and during each one the offensive team has a chance to gain ten yards.

End Zone: This is the area between the end line and the goal line. The bounds of the end line are the sidelines.

Field Goal: A field goal earns a team three points and happens when the ball is kicked between the uprights, and above the crossbar, on the goalpost.

Goal Line: The goal line is the front of the end zone. This line goes across the width of the field.

Incomplete Pass: A pass is incomplete if the ball hits the ground before it is caught.

Interception: An interception is when a member of the opposing team catches the ball.

Lines of Scrimmage: Two imaginary lines that extend across the field, parallel to the goal lines.

Offside: Each team is supposed to be behind their own side of the restraining line before the ball is snapped. If any part of a player's body goes beyond that line, he is offside.

Punt: A punt is when the ball is dropped, then kicked before it hits the ground.

Quarterback: The quarterback heads the team's offense.

Sack: A sack happens when the quarterback is tackled behind his line of scrimmage.

Touchdown: A touchdown is worth six points and is awarded when a player crosses the other team's goal line with the ball or catches a pass in their opponent's end zone, or picks up a loose ball in their opponent's end zone.

FOOTBALL FUN

Find these things that have to do with football in the word search below. Look up, down, backward, forward, and diagonally.

Astroturf **End zone** **Huddle** **Playbook** **Stadium**

Blitz **Goalpost** **Penalty** **Quarterback** **Touchdown**

```
P Z D Z X T H N Z O K T P G
E Y B H S B O S O C N L I O
J Q N W I B L U A P A T E A
E N O Z D N E B C Y A L E L
A C R I D W R B B H D I C P
R X F L N E Y O U D D L G O
F V A S T R O T U R F O D S
W G D R M K I H L P U V W T
T Z A V U I O U W A U S D N
Q U Q B I O Z T J Y N I O R
Q B B L D B V G P M M E Y T
U J Z P A B L I T Z I P P Z
D N B T T I P B M F W O A Y
G E F H S O H X L T G V T V
```

Answer on page 308

Design Your
WHAT'S ON YOUR MIND

What do you think each of these warriors is thinking as he prepares for battle? Fill out the thought bubbles above their heads!

Roller Coaster

Yahoo! Can you find the two pictures that are exactly alike?

Answer on page 309

UNDER THE BIG TOP

Use the clues below to complete this crossword puzzle about the circus.

ACROSS
1. Also known as the "Big Top"
4. A really big animal
5. Elephants eats these

DOWN
1. Acrobats swing from these
2. These performers have colorful clothes and big noses.
3. People walk across this, if they can balance.

Sudoku
ROCKING NUMBERS

Try to decode this sudoku. Fill in the empty squares so that each row, column, and square contains the numbers 1–9 only once.

6		9		1		2	3	
8		3	2					
1	4				3	6		8
5	8				6			1
		6	8	4	2	7		
	1	7	3				4	2
7			6			8	1	9
	6				2	4		3
		8		9		5		6

Answer on page 309

Would You Rather...

Which would you rather do?
Look at each pair of options. Think about them and check the things you would like best. Ask your friends, too!

Would you rather live...

☐ On the moon   or   ☐ On Mars?

Would you rather swim...

☐ With sharks   or   ☐ With whales?

Would you rather have...

☐ An elephant's trunk   or   ☐ A giraffe's neck?

Would you rather have dinner with...

☐ Your friend   or   ☐ Your teacher?

Ready, Set, Go!

Are you a super seeker? Put your eyes to the test and see if you can find 10 differences between the picture on the top and the one on the bottom.

Answer on page 309

CREEPY CRAWLERS

Use the clues to complete the crossword puzzle about types of bugs.

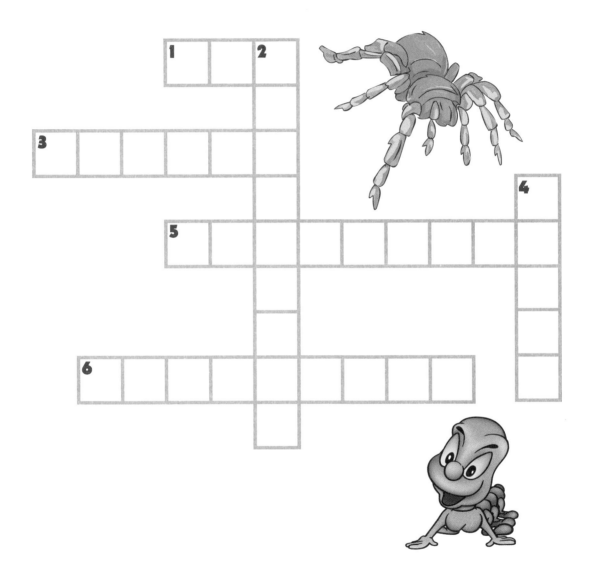

ACROSS
1. Digs a good picnic
3. Has eight legs
5. Has many, many legs
6. Has yellow and black stripes

DOWN
2. A hairy kind of spider
4. This type of worm sucks blood.

Answer on page 310

January

Fill in your calendar with all of the January birthdays you don't want to forget.

1	2	3	4	5	6	7
8	9	10	11	12	13	14
15	16	17	18	19	20	21
22	23	24	25	26	27	28
29	30	31				

TO DO:

February

Fill in your calendar with all of the February birthdays you don't want to forget.

1	2	3	4	5	6	7
8	9	10	11	12	13	14
15	16	17	18	19	20	21
22	23	24	25	26	27	28
29						

TO DO:

March

Fill in your calendar with all of the March birthdays you don't want to forget.

1	2	3	4	5	6	7
8	9	10	11	12	13	14
15	16	17	18	19	20	21
22	23	24	25	26	27	28
29	30	31				

TO DO:

_____

_____

_____

April

Fill in your calendar with all of the April birthdays you don't want to forget.

1	2	3	4	5	6	7
8	9	10	11	12	13	14
15	16	17	18	19	20	21
22	23	24	25	26	27	28
29	30					

TO DO:

_____

_____

_____

May

Fill in your calendar with all of the May birthdays you don't want to forget.

1	2	3	4	5	6	7
8	9	10	11	12	13	14
15	16	17	18	19	20	21
22	23	24	25	26	27	28
29	30	31				

TO DO:

June

Fill in your calendar with all of the June birthdays you don't want to forget.

1	2	3	4	5	6	7
8	9	10	11	12	13	14
15	16	17	18	19	20	21
22	23	24	25	26	27	28
29	30					

TO DO:

July

Fill in your calendar with all of the July birthdays you don't want to forget.

1	2	3	4	5	6	7
8	9	10	11	12	13	14
15	16	17	18	19	20	21
22	23	24	25	26	27	28
29	30	31				

TO DO:

_____

_____

_____

August

Fill in your calendar with all of the August birthdays you don't want to forget.

1	2	3	4	5	6	7
8	9	10	11	12	13	14
15	16	17	18	19	20	21
22	23	24	25	26	27	28
29	30	31				

TO DO:

September

Fill in your calendar with all of the September birthdays you don't want to forget.

1	2	3	4	5	6	7
8	9	10	11	12	13	14
15	16	17	18	19	20	21
22	23	24	25	26	27	28
29	30					

TO DO:

_____

_____

_____

October

Fill in your calendar with all of the October birthdays you don't want to forget.

1	2	3	4	5	6	7
8	9	10	11	12	13	14
15	16	17	18	19	20	21
22	23	24	25	26	27	28
29	30	31				

TO DO:

November

Fill in your calendar with all of the November birthdays you don't want to forget.

1	2	3	4	5	6	7
8	9	10	11	12	13	14
15	16	17	18	19	20	21
22	23	24	25	26	27	28
29	30					

TO DO:
_____
_____
_____

December

Fill in your calendar with all of the December birthdays you don't want to forget.

1	2	3	4	5	6	7
8	9	10	11	12	13	14
15	16	17	18	19	20	21
22	23	24	25	26	27	28
29	30	31				

TO DO:

Sudoku
SMART MATH

Use your math skills and try to decode this sudoku. Fill in the empty squares so that each row, column, and square contains the numbers 1–9 only once.

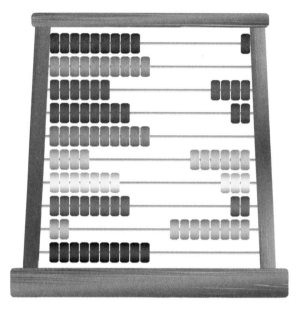

	8	4	6		5	7		9
				8				4
			2				3	
				9		6	7	
7			3	5	6			8
	6	5		4				
	1				3			
5								
2		8	9		1		5	4

Answer on page 310

Let's Play!

Solve this rebus puzzle to discover the name of something you would find in a park.

M + 1 - E + 🔑

🏏 - T + 🚶 - STAI

_ _ _ _ _ _ _ _

_ _ _ _ _

Making WORDS

Can you make at least 25 or more words from this phrase?

PINEWOOD DERBY

Design Your
THOUGHT PROCESS

What is this muddy guy thinking? Fill out the thought bubble above his head.

Cool Cowboy

Let's ride! Can you find the two pictures that are exactly alike?

Answer on page 311

Making Invisible Ink
How To
TIPS

This is a super-cool way to get secret messages to your pals! With invisible ink, no one will know what you are saying, unless you want them to. Be sure to ask an adult for help and supervision.

MATERIALS

- 1 Lemon
- Paintbrush
- White paper

DIRECTIONS

- Squeeze the lemon over a bowl to collect the lemon juice.

- Dip the paintbrush in the lemon juice and write a secret message on the paper.

- Once it is dry, bake your piece of paper at 325 degrees for three to five minutes.

- Take it out of oven and read it.

HOW DOES IT WORKS?

The heat burns the lemon juice, making it reappear on the paper.

Let's Draw a
Tyrannosaurus

On a separate piece of paper, follow these simple steps using a pencil and an eraser.

1 Use rectangles, ovals, squares, and triangles for the basic body, head, and tail. These are only guidelines, so draw them lightly.

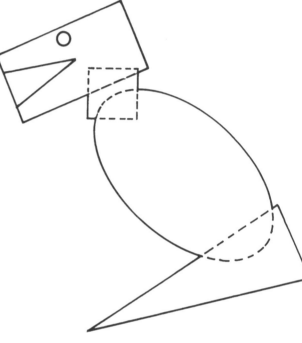

2 Using basic shapes as your guide, add small forearms and large legs, as shown.

3 Use your guidelines to form a clean outline of the basic body shape. As you work, erase any lines you don't need.

4 Put all the finishing touches on your drawing. Give Tyrannosaurus a ferocious look, big teeth, a mean look in its eye, and lots of skin effects.

PARKS AND RECREATION

Where do you like to hang when school's out? Find the names of these awesomely fun places in the word search below. Look up, down, backward, forward, and diagonally.

Aquarium

Beach

Campsite

Hiking trail

Lodge

Museum

Park

Ski slopes

Summer camp

Zoo

```
A H L F K Z L K B Z S H R T
Q K O K D C I J R I S Z R B
U T D O F S A C C A U H W H
A J G A F H R M A C P D Q D
R A E U Y A N U M V Q P M P
I H K Z N T G I P S M O M R
U H C A E B N S S D I A B M
M M O F S A I E I M C T U P
P G E B W Z K X T R L S E N
S R O B V N I N E E E V R Y
O X C Y W W H M Z U S Z V A
O S S H Y B M F M I P U H K
Z M I Z Z U X Q L R V Z M D
Q S K I S L O P E S D V M A
```

Answer on page 311

Create Your

COOLEST GUYS EVER LIST

Who are your favorite people to hang out with at school, at home, at the skate park—or anywhere, for that matter? Make a list of your closest buddies.

The Coolest Friends Ever:

_____   _____
_____   _____
_____   _____
_____   _____
_____   _____
_____   _____
_____   _____
_____   _____
_____   _____

Time Warp

Ever wonder what it must have been like to live in the past? What do you think you would have liked best about each of these eras?

The 1970's:

The 1800's:

The 1920's:

The 1980's:

The 1960's:

The 1990's:

Would You Rather...

Which would you rather do?
Look at each pair of options. Think about them and check the things you would like best. Ask your friends, too!

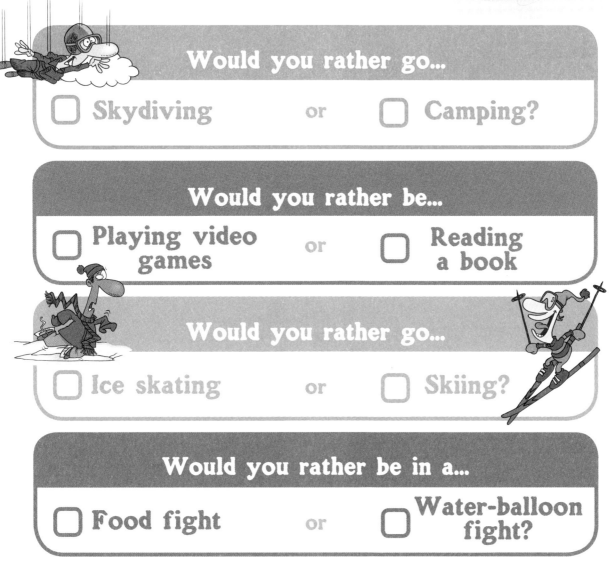

Would you rather go...

☐ Skydiving   or   ☐ Camping?

Would you rather be...

☐ Playing video games   or   ☐ Reading a book

Would you rather go...

☐ Ice skating   or   ☐ Skiing?

Would you rather be in a...

☐ Food fight   or   ☐ Water-balloon fight?

Making WORDS

Let's scramble some letters. Can you make 15 or more words of five or more letters from the following phrase?

WATER-BALLOON FIGHT

Answer on page 311

Write Your

Pretend you're living a long time ago—and that you are a dragon slayer! What's a typical day like for you? Write a blog entry about it here!

Once Upon a Time...

Caption your picture _____

_____

_____

_____

_____

_____

_____

_____

_____

_____

post by _____ time _____

Sudoku
STRAIGHT UP!

Try to decode this sudoku. Fill in the empty squares so that each row, column, and square contains the numbers 1–9 only once.

	2		5		7			
	5		9		6			
1				8			3	7
	1	4			5	8		
	7						1	
		2	1			6	9	
2	3			9				1
			2		3		8	
			7		1		2	

Water Park

Cowabunga, dude! Can you find the two pictures that are exactly alike?

Pool Maze

Follow the correct path through the maze to get the kid to the pool. What's the correct path, you ask? It's the one that is made up of life preservers only.

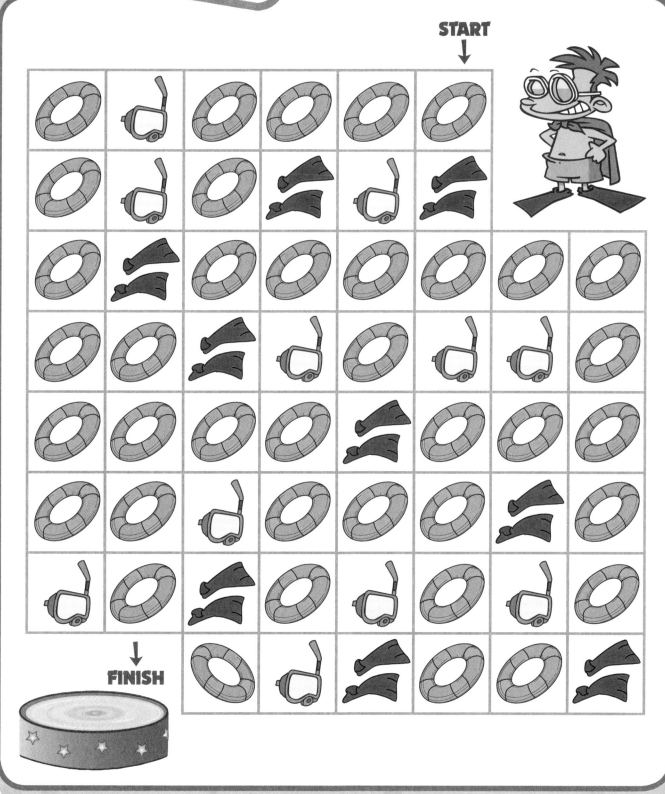

START

FINISH

Answer on page 312

MASKED BALL

BASEBALL BAT　　**HORSESHOE**　　**SNAKE**

DRUM　　**PAINTBRUSH**　　**STARFISH**

ELECTRIC FAN　　**SANDWICH**　　**TRASH CAN**

SCISSORS

Would You Rather...

Which would you rather do?
Look at each pair of options. Think about them and check the things you would like best. Ask your friends, too!

Would you rather have...

☐ 100 so-so friends   or   ☐ 2 REALLY great friends?

Would you rather have...

☐ A missing finger   or   ☐ An extra toe?

Would you rather...

☐ Play sports   or   ☐ Coach sports?

Would you rather go...

☐ Skydiving   or   ☐ Bungee jumping?

Create Your
SILLY
CONVERSATION

This monster just got himself a new puppy! What do you think the monster thinks of his new pet? And what do you think the puppy things about being adopted by a monster? Fill in their thoughts in the speech bubbles!

The Great Outdoors

Are you a super seeker? Put your eyes to the test and see if you can find 10 differences between the picture on the top and the one on the bottom.

Answer on page 312

SUMMER CAMP

Use the clues about summer camp to solve the crossword puzzle.

ACROSS
4. Helps you cook things when you're out in the wilderness
5. You can float on the water in this
7. You might sleep in this
8. An adult who works at the camp

DOWN
1. You toast this over a campfire.
2. Tell this kind of story around a fire to spook the campers
3. Holds your water
6. Paddle this by yourself or with another person

Answer on page 313

Ban Bullying
How To
TIPS

Bullying is no joke and it should be taken seriously. Here are some tips to help you cope.

What To Do If You Are BEING BULLIED

- Tell an adult, like a teacher or a parent.
- Ask your friends to stand by you and help.
- Choose your words carefully, so that you can defend yourself.
- Stay calm and confident.
- Ignore the bully and walk away. Fighting back will only make the problem worse.

Remember: Lots of kids encounter some form of bullying. You are not alone. No one deserves to be bullied.

What To Do If You WITNESS BULLYING

- Speak up on behalf of the person being bullied.
- Ask the bully to stop.
- Comfort the person being bullied and offer friendship and a shoulder to lean on.
- Walk away and get help.
- Find an adult who can help the situation.

What To Do If You ARE THE BULLY

- Talk to someone you trust and get advice on how to better get along with others.
- Apologize to the kids you have bullied.
- Before you bully, think about whether your words will help or hurt another student.
- Don't bully because you are pressured into doing so. No one likes a bully.

TYPES OF CLOTHES

Find these types of clothes in the word search below. Look up, down, backward, forward, and diagonally.

Hat	Jeans	Pajamas	Shoes	Socks
Jacket	Necktie	Shirt	Shorts	Trousers

```
V C A V P T S H O R T S S S
R T L S E K E J J A N L A H
A K E K A J B I H R R L M M
K R C F G E L W T Q Z B A Y
J A R G M O R S I K M B J W
J E S R E S U O R T C S A P
B T A G Q M B C M L H E P W
Y G A N K R U K X O X X N W
T R I H S S U S E Q X D F N
D H K G I T E S S P X W H O
Y K K R R B X Z Q V B O E W
I S T A I R M K R D R J P L
W L G U D B S T G V B A U R
Q K R W N G S N R S U C S S
```

Answer on page 313

Design Your
ULTIMATE
T-SHIRT

Do you have a favorite band or a retro graphic that you'd love to sport on a t-shirt? Design it here!

MY PET DINO

Fill in the blanks to complete this silly story about what it might be like to have a pet dinosaur. Pick a NOUN, ADJECTIVE, or VERB from the word bank to place in a corresponding blank, or think of your own wacky words!

I've been begging my parents forever to let me get a pet dinosaur,

and they finally agreed! My dinosaur is _____ and a little bit
[ADJECTIVE]

_____ and he loves to _____ all day long! My sister likes
[ADJECTIVE]   [VERB]

to _____ right along with him. The only problem is that he keeps
[VERB]

chewing up my _____ and _____. One day I caught
[NOUN]   [NOUN]

my dinosaur about to_____ the _____!
[VERB]   [NOUN]

WORD BANK

ADJECTIVES

wooly
itchy
silly
scared
gentle
weak
dumb
sweet
brave

NOUNS

watermelon
baseball cap
football
homework
sweater
computer
cereal
t-shirt
bed

VERBS

chomp
jump
jog
nap
sew
read
ride
bow
sit

Create Your
THINGS THAT GO LIST

How many vehicles—of any kind—can you think of? Set a timer for two minutes. Then, see how many vehicles you can name in that time! Test your friends, too.

Cat Maze

Follow the correct path through the maze to get the cat to the mouse. What's the correct path, you ask? It's the one that is made up of balls of yarn only.

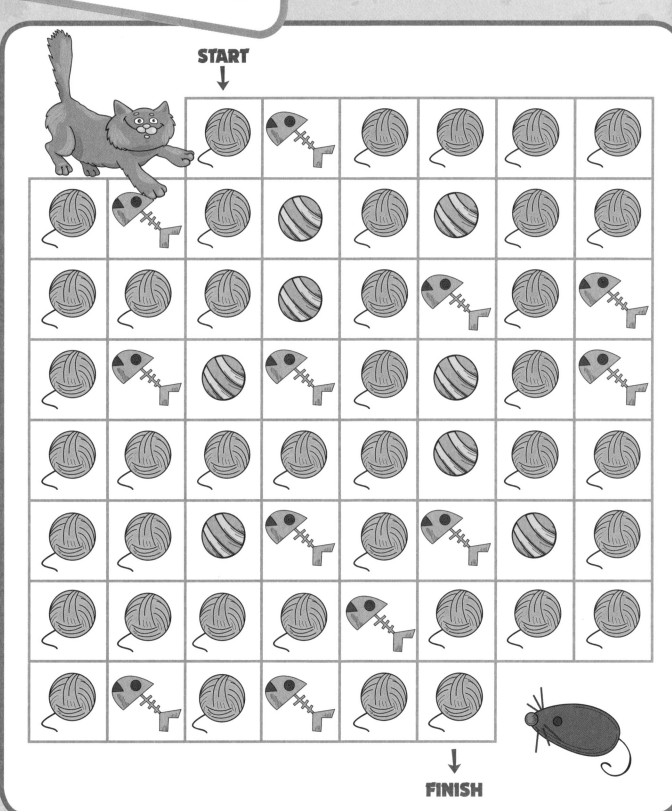

START

FINISH

Answer on page 313

Speedy Train

All aboard! Can you find the two pictures that are exactly alike?

Answer on page 313

Let's Draw a
Minotaur

On a separate piece of paper, follow these simple steps using a pencil and an eraser.

1 Begin with a circle for the head and add more circular shapes for the body, legs, and feet.

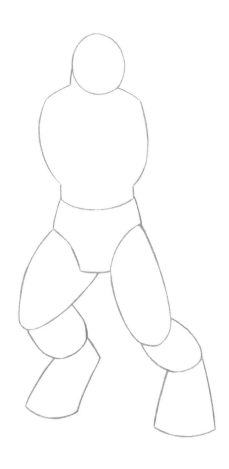

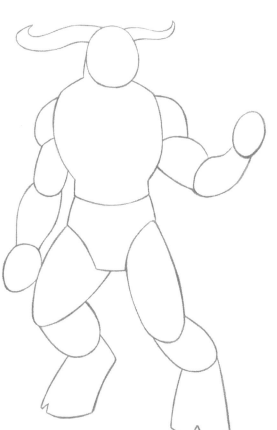

2 Add horns to both sides of the head, arms, and hands. Draw the split in the hooves on the feet.

3 Add straps on the arms and a loincloth. Erase any unwanted guidelines.

4 Finalize the drawing by adding the axe, belt details, and armbands. Complete with color and shading.

LET'S PARTY!

Get your party on! Find the names of these things that have to do with parties in the word search below. Look up, down, backward, forward, and diagonally.

Balloons **Cake** **Candy** **Friends** **Holiday**
Birthday **Candles** **Costume** **Gifts** **Sleepover**

```
Z S S S S V V O G A A B Y C
I H X L E G X L U U I W A V
D O Q E L Y B L I R C K A K
D Q S E D O W Z T L E O T F
J C M P N Z H H B S G R K L
W S U O A Y D H O L I D A Y
V Y A V C A S N O O L L A B
E T E E Y D G V A D Y S Z Q
N M C R N U T I B A M F H X
K D U E P F F S F C Z C E C
J D I T A H E B P T P A H U
G R F A S D A Z O Y S N J P
F V D D T O L J M V A D K M
U Q M Q B Q C D X B S Y Z P
```

Sudoku
WHAT'S YOUR IQ?

Try to decode this sudoku. Fill in the empty squares so that each row, column, and square contains the numbers 1–9 only once.

	7				2			
		1		6	9	7		5
					7	8	6	9
					1			6
	5		6		3		7	
8		2	9					
4	2	7	3					
9		6	2	4		3		
			7				4	

Design Your Own

RACE CAR
COMPETITION

On your mark, get set, finish this racetrack! Draw in the rest of the track, the cars, and the crowd!

FOOD FIGHT!

Fill in the blanks to complete this silly story about what might happen in a food fight. Pick a NOUN, ADJECTIVE, or VERB from the word bank to place in a corresponding blank, or think of your own wacky words!

It was a normal day in the school cafeteria. That is, until my friend

threw a _____ and a _____ across the room! It _____ed
　　　　　　[NOUN]　　　　　　　[NOUN]　　　　　　　　　　　[VERB]

the _____ and totally made a _____ sound. Some
　　　　[NOUN]　　　　　　　　　　　[ADJECTIVE]

people felt completely _____ and others got into it. It was
　　　　　　　　　　　[ADJECTIVE]

so _____! The worst thing that was _____ed in the food
　　　[ADJECTIVE]　　　　　　　　　　　　　[VERB]

fight was definitely the _____, because it _____ed all over
　　　　　　　　　　　　　[NOUN]　　　　　　　　　　[VERB]

the _____!
　　　[NOUN]

WORD BANK

ADJECTIVES

gross
stinky
squishy
slimy
neat
weird
squiggly
yellow
hot

NOUNS

pretzel
yogurt
pickle
spider
book
cheese
skirt
toilet paper
umbrella

VERBS

squish
leap
yell
soar
sniff
jump
slurp
yawn
bump

Old West

Are you a super seeker? Put your eyes to the test and see if you can find 10 differences between the picture on the top and the one on the bottom.

Answer on page 314

Pirate TERMS

Arrrggghhhh! Here's the lingo ye need to know if you want to talk like a true pirate! You'll be swabbin' the deck in no time!

Ahoy: What you yell when you want to attract someone's attention, sort of like "hey!".

Arrr!: An exclamation.

Aye: Yes.

Black Spot: A black spot is left on something by a pirate to indicate a threat to his enemy.

Blimey!: An exclamation a pirate uses to express surprise.

Davy Jones' Locker: Davy Jones was a famous pirate who supposedly sank every ship he took over. Davy Jones' locker is a made-up place at the bottom of the ocean. When your ship is sunk and you die in the sea, you are said to have been sent to Davy Jones' locker.

Fire in the Hole: This is the warning that is shouted before a cannon is fired.

Handsomely: This means to do something quickly or correctly.

Ho: This expression is used to indicate that you have spotted something ahead, such as, "Land, ho!"

Hornswaggle: Cheat.

Marooned: To be stranded. Usually used when one is stranded on an island.

Me: My.

Mutiny: An uprising against the person in charge (usually the captain of the ship).

Pillage: To rob someone.

Piracy: A robbery committed at sea is piracy.

Plunder: Another word for pillage.

Run a Shot Across the Bow: This is what you say when you want one of your mates to fire a warning shot.

Sea Legs: To be able to adjust to the motion of being on a ship at sea.

Shiver Me Timbers!: A pirate says this when he is totally shocked by something.

Swab: To clean the deck of a ship.

Walk the Plank: When a pirate takes over a ship, he will tell the pirates already on board to walk the plank, meaning, they have to walk the plank, into the water, and give up their ship.

Ye: You.

SHIVER ME TIMBERS!

Use the clues about pirates to solve the crossword puzzle.

ACROSS
1. Pirates wear this on an eye
4. Another word for "my"
6. Sometimes pirates will give other pirates this type of "dot"
7. Weapon commonly used by pirates for defense
8. What pirates say when they see land
9. A pirate's main vehicle of transportation

DOWN
2. Means "yes"
3. This is shot out of a cannon
5. Some pirates have these in their ears

Answer on page 314

Create Your
SUPER
HEROES
LIST

Who are some of your heroes—the people you admire the most? It can be anybody, real or not. List why each person is a hero to you.

My Heroes:

_____ _____
_____ _____
_____ _____
_____ _____
_____ _____
_____ _____
_____ _____
_____ _____
_____ _____

Space FACTS

Want to expand your knowledge about the world beyond our planet? Then take a look at these fun space facts!

The asteroid belt is a strip of asteroids, or rocks, floating around the solar system. The belt is made up of material that didn't make it into the planets during the formation of the solar system—the asteroids were too close to Jupiter's strong pull of gravity and were led away from all other planets.

A probe called Luna 1 was launched in 1959 by the Soviet Union. It was supposed to land on the moon and collect soil samples, but it missed its destination and has since been lost in space.

The sun's surface is constantly releasing jest of gas, known as solar flares. These flares can react with Earth's atmosphere to create dazzling colors—in the northern hemisphere; this is called the Northern Lights, or Aurora Borealis.

Constellation Creation

Using the stars on this page, draw lines to form as many constellations as you know!

Underwater Swimmer

Solve this rebus puzzle to discover the name of something swimmers should look out for.

$$S + \text{🎵} - P + K$$

$$-B + T + \text{🃏} - J$$

_ _ _ _ _ _ _

_ _ _ _ _ _

Answer on page 315

Monster Maze

Even monsters hate bad weather. Follow the path made up from numbers **1** through **25** to help the monster get to the house.

Start →

1	2	3	4	19	5	2
2	8	7	5	6	4	3
3	12	13	6	7	8	9
4	5	7	8	9	10	11
1	6				24	23
3	7			**Finish** ←	25	24
9	8				3	23
10	20				2	22
11	3	18	16	12	18	21
12	13	14	15	10	6	20
20	21	15	16	17	18	19
19	18	17	16	15	14	13

Answer on page 315

225

Crime Fighter

Are you a super seeker? Put your eyes to the test and see if you can find 10 differences between the picture on the top and the one on the bottom.

Answer on page 315

CAMPING

Pack up your gear and get ready for some campfire craziness! Find the names of these camping terms in the word search below. Look up, down, backward, forward, and diagonally.

Backpack
Cabin
Campfire   **Fishing**   **Sleeping bag**   **Tent**
Campground   **Ghost stories**   **Smores**   **Woods**

C M T O I Y C K O N B G E W
D O Z H W R C Y Y W H G R N
N W R C T A O T J O P P I G
G S V D P F S H S O Z J F R
U S M K N T B T A D C O P W
B R C O C U S X A S H F M X
M A V A R T O T N E T D A V
B R B K O E A R Q E M H C O
M I O R G E S G G T M N R O
N C I G A B G N I P E E L S
O E F I S H I N G B M C T Z
S U G P Z L I K R F X A I H
M W K E S V U M R O X N C U
Y Z D S X U M J A T A W D L

Design Your Own

SCUBA ADVENTURE

Fill the ocean with sea creatures for this scuba diver to encounter. The weirder, the better! What kind of things would you want to see on a scuba trip?

Let's Draw an
Aston Martin

On a separate piece of paper, follow these simple steps using a pencil and an eraser.

1 Begin by sketching the basic shapes of the body. Draw through your shapes to establish form. Then draw two tires.

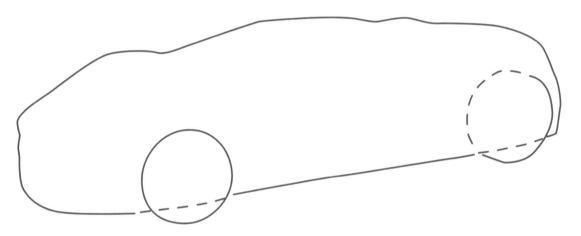

2 Erase the unwanted lines near the tires. Add more detail with shapes of the grille, lights, windows, and door. Draw wheel wells.

3 Continue by adding more detail with crisp clean lines. Add mirrors and cockpit details. Draw the cool rims and use lines to show form on the hood and side panel.

4 Choose a gold color for your Aston Martin and black for the interior. Show shadows and reflections with a darker tone, and add highlights with lighter tones. Finish off the rims and hit the road!

Would You Rather...

Which would you rather do?
Look at each pair of options. Think about them and check the things you would like best. Ask your friends, too!

Would you rather watch...

☐ Comedians   or   ☐ Cartoons?

Would you rather smell...

☐ Pie   or   ☐ Beef jerky?

Would you rather...

☐ Snort milk out of your nose   or   ☐ Burp?

Would you rather have...

☐ Freckles   or   ☐ A tan?

Tie a Tie!
How To
TIPS

You might not be bombarded with invitations for fancy parties right now, but learning how to tie a tie is essential for any dude's future. Practice!

Steps

1. Drape the tie around your neck, so that the ends rest on your chest.

2. The wide end of the tie should be on your right and the other end should be on your left.

3. Cross the wide end over the other end.

4. Now bring the wide end underneath the narrow end from left to right.

5. Next, pull the wide end over from right to left.

6. Put the wide end under the knot.

7. Bring the wide end down and pass the loop in front. Make sure that the knot is tightened.

8. Pull the narrow end down gently and, at the same time, move the knot up until it reaches the center of the collar.

Create Your

FOOTBALL STRATEGY

It's time for football season! You've jus[t] been hired as the main coach of the best football team in the country. Draw one of your team's signature plays.

TOUCHDOWN

-10 -20 -30 -40

10- 20- 30- 40-

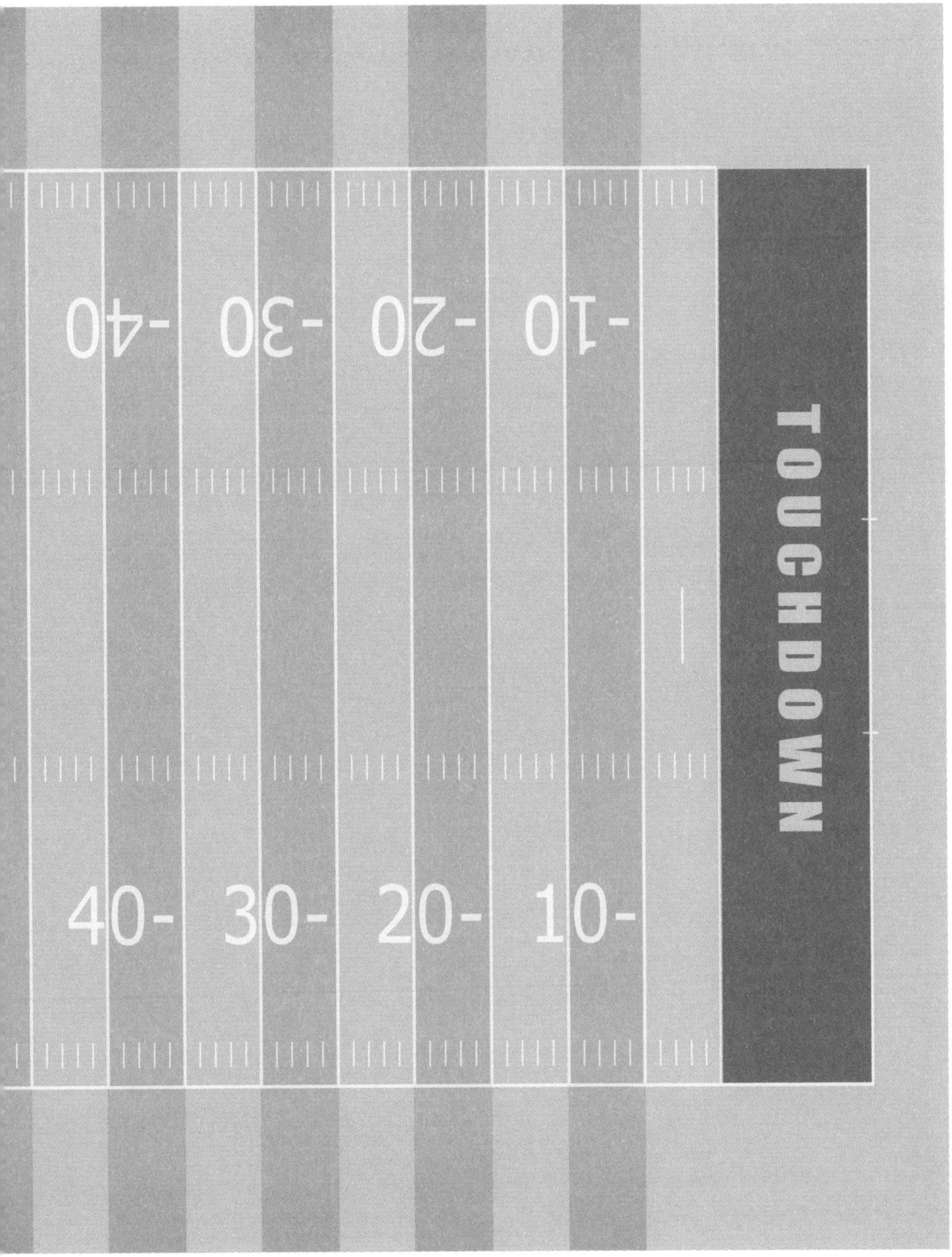
TOUCHDOWN
10
20
30
40
10
20
30
40

Wet Weather

Answer on page 316

Create Your FAVE JUNK FOOD LIST

If junk food was healthy and you could eat as much of it as you wanted, what would you choose? Make a list of your favorite junk foods.

My Favorite Junk Foods:

Are you a super seeker? Put your eyes to the test and see if you can find 10 differences between the picture on the top and the one on the bottom.

Answer on page 316

Car Talk
How To
TIPS

Need to know what a spark plug does? The answer to that and other engine questions are right here!

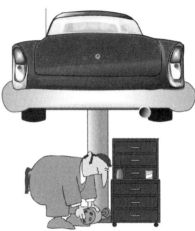

Engine

The engine converts energy into useful mechanical motion. It burns fuel to create heat and then propel the car.

Spark Plug

The spark plug makes the spark that ignites the air/fuel mixture so that combustion happens. This has to happen at the right moment for everything to work correctly.

Cylinder

The core of the engine; the part the holds the pistons.

Valves

The valves open at the right time to let in air and fuel and to let out exhaust.

Piston

A piston is a piece of metal that moves up and down to help change gas into energy.

Let's Draw a
Formula One Racecar

On a separate piece of paper, follow these simple steps using a pencil and an eraser.

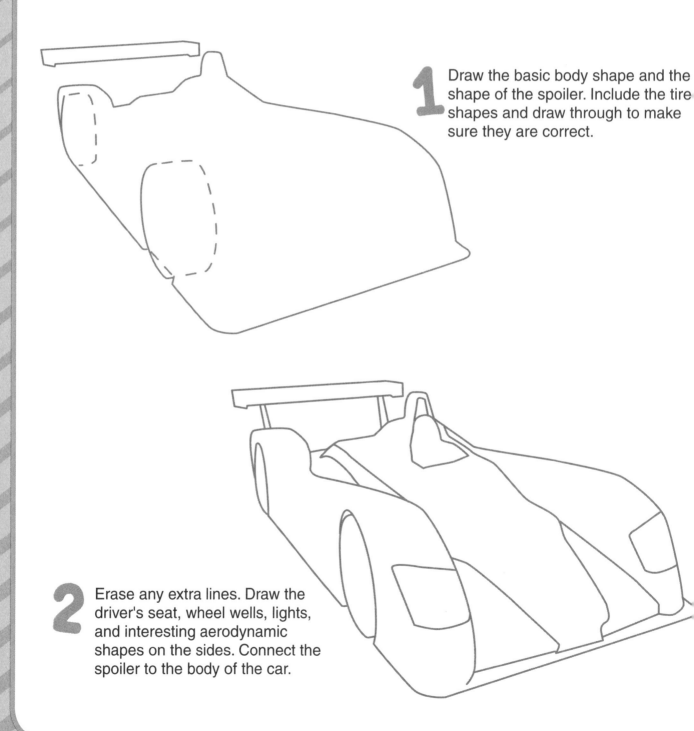

1 Draw the basic body shape and the shape of the spoiler. Include the tire shapes and draw through to make sure they are correct.

2 Erase any extra lines. Draw the driver's seat, wheel wells, lights, and interesting aerodynamic shapes on the sides. Connect the spoiler to the body of the car.

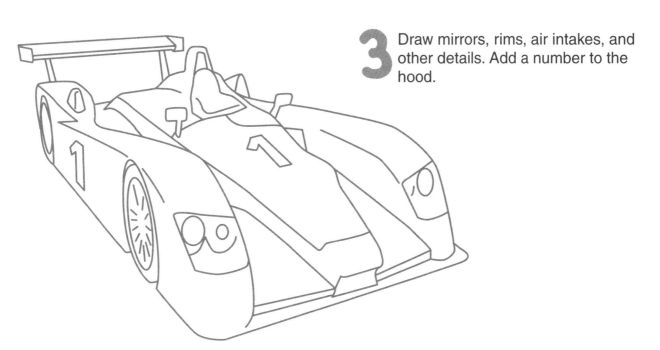

3 Draw mirrors, rims, air intakes, and other details. Add a number to the hood.

4 A silver and red color combination is a great choice for this car. Make sure you blend the red into the silver for an extra-cool look. This car is ready to win the race!

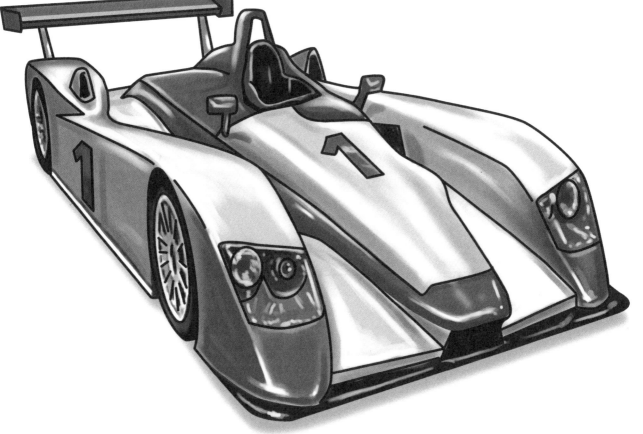

Write the letter that comes THREE LETTERS AFTER each letter shown below to decode and solve the riddle.

T E X Q   T L R I A   V L R

D B Q   F C   B S B O V

X R Q L J L Y F I B

L K   Q E B   O L X A

T X P   M F K H ?

X   M F K H

\- Z X O   K X Q F L K

Answer on page 316

INTO THE WOODS

ALARM CLOCK   CHICKEN DRUMSTICK   LOCK

BIGFOOT   FISHBOWL   RULER

BOW TIE   FORK   TREE ORNAMENT

ICE SKATES (2)

Answer on page 316

Design Your Own
WHAT'S IN A NAME?

Wonder what it would be like if you had a different name? Here's your chance to try out some new names. List them!

Possible New Names:

_____   _____

_____   _____

_____   _____

_____   _____

_____   _____

_____   _____

_____   _____

_____   _____

Sudoku
SUPER SOLVER

Try to decode this sudoku. Fill in the empty squares so that each row, column, and square contains the numbers 1–9 only once.

4		2	5	7				1
		2					7	
		1		4	3	5		
1	4				8			
3							6	
	9				7	1		
6	1	9	3					
	4			5				
2			4	1	5			6

LOST in the LIBRARY

Fill in the blanks to complete this silly story about what it might be like to be lost in a gigantic library. Pick a NOUN, ADJECTIVE, or VERB from the word bank to place in a corresponding blank, or think of your own wacky words!

I was reading a book in a quiet corner and I got locked in the library at night.

I was in the _____ section when I completely forgot to _____. I
[NOUN]   [VERB]

was so _____ that I decided to _____ right away! Before I knew
[ADJECTIVE]   [VERB]

it, a _____ approached and told me to _____! The library turns
[NOUN]   [VERB]

into a _____ and _____ place during the night.
[ADJECTIVE]   [ADJECTIVE]

WORD BANK

ADJECTIVES	NOUNS	VERBS
scary	magazine	leap
short	computer	scream
purple	machine	drop
thick	guard	free fall
loud	present	sleep
smart	truck	sing
squiggly	dust ball	slurp
cool	toilet	blow
hot	hot dog	spit

Pool Party

Are you a super seeker? Put your eyes to the test and see if you can find 10 differences between the picture on the top and the one on the bottom.

Answer on page 317

Design Your Own
SLIMY SUNDAE

Turn this ice-cream sundae into the grossest, smelliest, most heinous sundae in history! Add worms, ants, tar—whatever you think will make it the grossest!

Winter Wonderland

Solve this rebus puzzle to discover the name of something that strikes in the dead of winter.

Would You Rather...

Which would you rather do?
Look at each pair of options. Think about them and check the things you would like best. Ask your friends, too!

Would you rather have...

☐ The ability to fly   or   ☐ The ability to be invisible?

Would you rather eat...

☐ 25 hot dogs   or   ☐ 25 hamburgers?

Would you rather be...

☐ Really, really tall   or   ☐ Really, really short?

Would you rather eat...

☐ A tarantula   or   ☐ A cricket?

School Maze

Follow the correct path through the maze to get the boy to his locker. What's the correct path, you ask? It's the one that is made up of backpacks only!

START

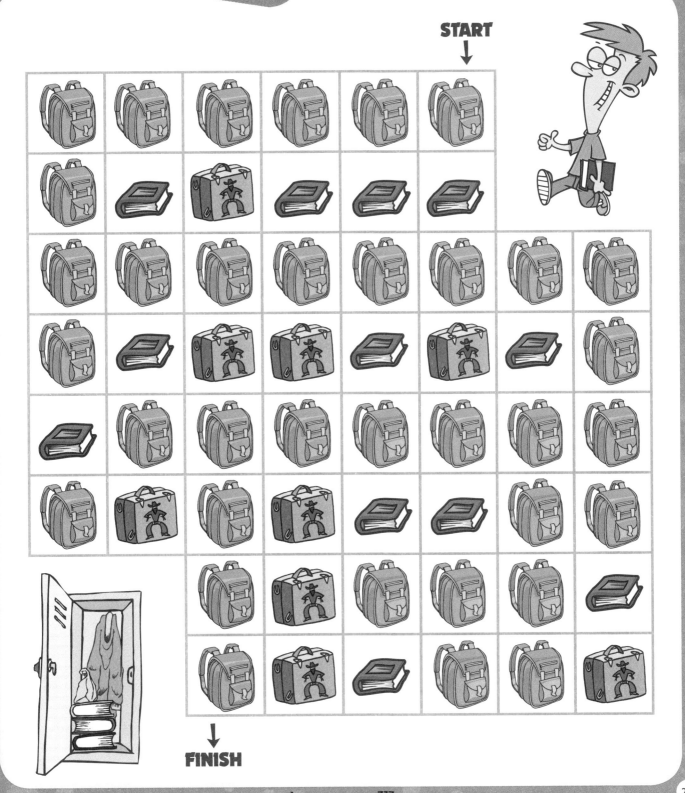

FINISH

Scene of the Crime

How To TIPS

Do you devour crime shows and reality cop shows? Do you dream of taking down a perp? Find out all you need to know about fingerprints right here!

HOW TO FINGERPRINT A PERP

- Shade in an area of paper with the point of a pencil.
- Rub your finger into the spot.
- Stick the sticky side of a piece of tape on the finger.
- Tape that to a clean piece of white paper.
- Label it.
- Repeat the process with all of the fingers.
- An alternative, messier method: press each fingertip into an inkpad.

DUSTING FOR PRINTS

Stuff You will need:
- Drinking glass
- Cocoa powder
- Small soft brush
- Transparent tape
- Five Sheets of light-colored paper

1. Press your finger on the side of a drinking glass. Tip: Sticky or oily fingers make better prints.
2. Coat the prints with a dusting of cocoa powder.
3. Brush gently on the glass. The excess powder will disappear, but the fingerprints will remain.
4. Place the sticky side of the tape on the dusted fingerprint. Then tape it to the paper.
5. If you're dusting for prints on a dark surface, use baby powder instead of cocoa powder.

TRY OUT YOUR FINGERPRINTS HERE:

Frenzy Fire Truck

Vroom, vroom! Can you find the two pictures that are exactly alike?

Answer on page 318

Design Your Own

DESTINATION: WEIRD!

This is the hottest new design in vacation resorts! It's a little odd... but that's what gives it its charm! Can you come up with a list of possible names for this unique new style of architecture?

CONSTRUCTION SITE

Use the clues about construction sites to figure out this crossword puzzle.

ACROSS
1. A big vehicle that hauls dirt
4. You dig this up; it's brown
5. You wear this to protect your noggin

DOWN
2. This makes concrete
3. This is used to build foundations
6. These pull up the dirt

Sudoku
MAGIC NUMBERS

Try to decode this sudoku. Fill in the empty squares so that each row, column, and square contains the numbers 1–9 only once.

4		5						
6		7	3	4			1	
8			1					4
	2			3	1			
7	3						8	5
			7	5		3		
3					6			7
	4			2	7	5		8
						4		1

Let's Draw a
Vampire

On a separate piece of paper, follow these simple steps using a pencil and an eraser.

1 Begin with basic shapes for the head, body, and legs.

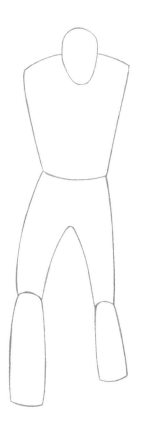

2 Add arms, hands, and feet. Create guidelines on the face.

3 Draw details to the body and face. Add the cape. Erase the guidelines.

4 Enhance the drawing by adding color, shading, and details to the clothing.

Write Your

BLOG

If you could invent something, what would it be? What would it do? What would you call it? Write a blog entry about it here!

Invent It!

Caption your picture _____

_____

_____

_____

_____

_____

_____

_____

_____

_____

post by_____ time _____

Tricky Teammate

Answer on page 318

WHAT STINKS?

Fill in the blanks to complete this silly story about something colossally smelly. Pick a NOUN, ADJECTIVE, or VERB from the word bank to place in a corresponding blank, or think of your own wacky words!

Woooooo, that is some stinky smell! I left a _____ in my _____
[NOUN] [NOUN]

and totally forgot all about it. Then, I smelled a _____ odor. It
[ADJECTIVE]

made me completely _____ and the dude with the locker next
[ADJECTIVE]

to mine was going to _____ when he whiffed it. Then I went to
[VERB]

_____ it right away—let's hope the _____ is gone!
[VERB] [NOUN]

WORD BANK

ADJECTIVES

smelly
gross   yummy
sweet   sour
nasty   crazy
yucky   weird

NOUNS

tuna fish
cheese   pickle
dirty sock   carrot
hot dog   muffin
salad   scarf

VERBS

puke   sit
gag   jump
spit   pass out
faint   cough
laugh

PREHISTORIC PREY

Ever wonder what it was like to roam the earth in the prehistoric days? These dudes know all about it! Find the names of these dinosaurs in the word search. Look up, down, backward, forward, and diagonally.

Allosaurus   Pteranodon
Avimimus   Stegosaurus
Deinonychus   Triceratops
Iguanodon   Tyrannosaurus
Megalosaurus   Velociraptor

```
I  T  S  A  L  L  O  S  A  U  R  U  S  V
G  Y  C  U  W  D  Y  Z  D  Z  S  M  E  G
U  R  P  A  H  P  H  F  E  P  D  L  V  J
A  A  T  T  M  C  O  C  O  C  O  B  A  S
N  N  G  U  E  P  Y  T  Z  C  S  V  D  U
O  N  X  L  J  R  A  N  I  K  I  N  I  R
D  O  O  N  K  R  A  R  O  M  F  S  X  U
O  S  W  I  E  C  A  N  I  N  T  W  E  A
N  A  K  C  N  P  K  M  O  Y  I  C  W  S
J  U  I  M  T  O  U  L  F  D  O  E  R  O
G  R  L  O  B  S  U  G  W  U  O  P  D  G
T  U  R  X  M  G  S  M  G  U  A  N  C  E
T  S  R  X  R  G  H  T  G  O  A  P  C  T
S  U  R  U  A  S  O  L  A  G  E  M  M  S
```

Answer on page 319

Design Your

WHO'S COMING TO TOWN?

This looks like a quaint little town, doesn't it? Well, a pack of zombies, ghouls, and monsters are about to invade! Do some drawing and depict what the town will look like AFTER the ghoul fest!

Weather FACTS

Sure, we've all been caught in a downpour or maybe the occasional thunderstorm, but have you ever had to deal with a typhoon? Lots of people in different parts of the world have! Sharpen your knowledge of extreme weather with these facts!

A typhoon is a powerful storm that begins over a large body of water. A hurricane is generally the same thing. The difference is that typhoons are most common in the Pacific Ocean, and hurricanes in the Atlantic Ocean.

The sight of a lightning bolt and the sound of thunder are actually the same thing. When lighting strikes, it opens a "crack" in the air. When the lightning disappears, the air moves back together again and created a loud sound. The only reason we see lightning first is because light travels faster than sound!

Tornadoes can happen on every continent except Antarctica, but they famously and most commonly occur in a region of the United States nicknamed "Tornado Alley." This describes the region of the country roughly between the Appalachian and Rocky Mountain ranges.

DISASTER STRIKES!

Use the clues about natural disasters to complete this crossword puzzle.

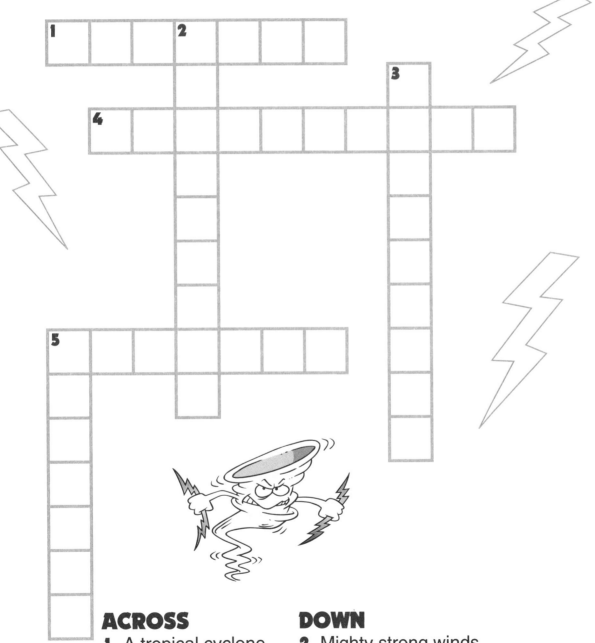

ACROSS
1. A tropical cyclone
4. The ground shakes
5. Looks like a funnel

DOWN
2. Mighty strong winds
3. Rocks and mud and debris tumble
5. Massively devastating wave

Basketball BASICS

It's time to hit the court and shoot some hoops. But, do you know all there is to know about basketball? Brush up with these basketball basics!

THE BASICS

- In a basketball game, there are two teams with five players on each team.
- The way to score is to get the ball in the opposing team's basket.
- The ball can be passed, thrown, or dribbled in any direction.
- The ball is out of bounds when it touches any of the sidelines around the court.
- Dribbling is when you bounce the ball and run down the court at the same time, without holding the ball or carrying it. If you use both hands to dribble, that is called double dribbling. That's not allowed and if you do it, the other team gets the ball.
- If you pick up the ball while dribbling, you are only allowed to take one step, with one foot, then shoot. If you step with both feet, that is called traveling. Again, not allowed.

- There are three places you can shoot the ball from: behind the three-point line (or the arc around the basket), inside the arc (which is worth two points), or from the free-throw line (free throws are worth one point).
- A foul is when you hit or touch someone on the other team while guarding him.
- If you get fouled, you get to take two shots from the free throw line.
- There are four quarters in a basketball game. Each quarter is twelve minutes long.
- The rim of a regulation basketball hoop is eighteen inches in diameter and ten feet off the floor.
- The backboard is what the net and rim are attached to.
- A slam dunk is when a player leaps into the air and slams the ball into the net from above (with their hands over the rim).

Design Your B-BALL GREATS

Now that you know the b-ball basics, you can go back to watching your favorite players slam dunk their way to fame! Who are your favorite pro basketball players? What about non-pros? List them all here!

My Basketball Heroes:

_____   _____
_____   _____
_____   _____
_____   _____
_____   _____
_____   _____
_____   _____
_____   _____

Let's Jump!

Solve this rebus puzzle to discover the name of something that you jump from.

_ _ _ _ _ _ _

_ _ _ _ _ _

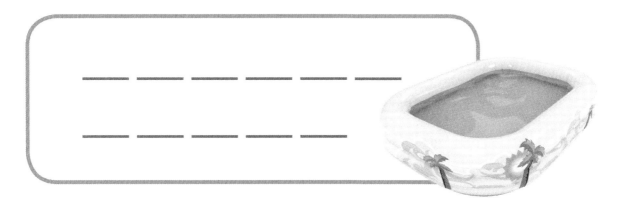

Mixed-up STORIES

The story below is listed in the wrong order. Write the numbers of the correct order in the spaces below.

A man takes a taxi from an airport to a subway station.

1

A man walks down a street to his friend's house.

2

A man drives a car to an airport.

3

_____

_____

_____

_____

_____

_____

A man takes an airplane from one side of the world to the other.

4

A man takes the subway to a bus stop.

5

A man takes a bus to the end of the street.

6

Answer on page 319

Sports Game

Are you a super seeker? Put your eyes to the test and see if you can find 10 differences between the picture on the top and the one on the bottom.

PEANUTS

PEAS

Let's Draw an
Iguanodon

On a separate piece of paper, follow these simple steps using a pencil and an eraser.

1 Start with a large free-form oval for the body. Add a smaller oval for the head and a triangle shape for most of the neck. Connect the neck and body with a short line, as shown.

2 Add the basic shapes for the arms, legs, pointy claws, and tail. Note the spike pointing upward on top of each hand. Don't forget the mouth!

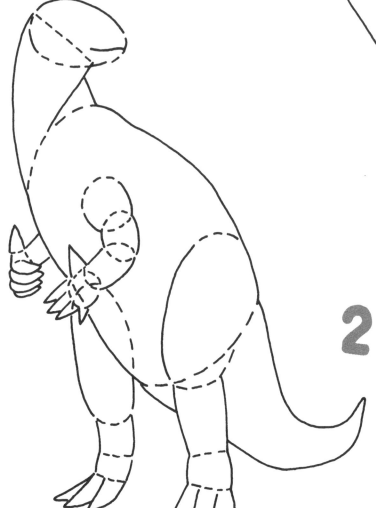

3 Add an eye and a nostril. Then erase unneeded guidelines as you blend the shapes and lines into a smooth outline of Iguanodon.

4 Complete your drawing by adding rows of shading and skin details. Now this Iguanodon is ready to pound the prehistoric pavement!

Sudoku
BRAIN SCRAMBLER

Try to decode this sudoku. Fill in the empty squares so that each row, column, and square contains the numbers 1–9 only once.

		1			4		2	
	8	7	6		9			
4			5	1	7			
1	2					6	5	4
	7	5					1	3
			1	7	5			8
			2		7	9	3	
	4		3			1		

Answer on page 320

HAUNTED HAYRIDE

Fill in the blanks to complete this silly story about what it might be like to go on a haunted hayride. Pick a NOUN, ADJECTIVE, or VERB from the word bank to place in a corresponding blank, or think of your own wacky words!

I went on the absolute most _____ haunted hayride!
[ADJECTIVE]

I was so _____. It started out in a _____ and then
[ADJECTIVE]   [NOUN]

ended up in a _____. I had to _____ just to stop myself
[NOUN]   [VERB]

from shaking when it was all over. All my _____s thought
[NOUN]

I was being a _____ _____! If I ever went on another
[ADJECTIVE]   [NOUN]

one, I would definitely bring a _____!
[NOUN]

WORD BANK

ADJECTIVES

vicious
scary
funny
tiny
warm
confused
crowded
short
yellow

NOUNS

garbage can
gym
barn
friend
rink
backpack
flower
cupboard
cat

VERBS

scream
fall
tumble
howl
flip
hide
yawn
sneeze
yelp

Plain Batty Maze

Follow the path from **Start** to **Finish** to guide the vampire bats to the cave.

START

FINISH

Answer on page 320

Design Your FIGHTIN' WORDS

What are these siblings arguing about? Fill in their banter in the speech bubbles!

Magic Potion!
How To
TIPS

Want to wow your pals with a real live magic potion? Here's your chance!

MATERIALS

- **Large Pot**
- **Water**
- **Baking soda**
- **Vinegar**
- **Tablespoon**
- **Pan**

DIRECTIONS

- Place the pot on the pan, this way the potions won't spill all over. There's nothing worse than a messy magic potion!

- Fill the pot with two tablespoons of water.

- Stir in a tablespoon of baking soda until it dissolves.

- Pour two tablespoons of vinegar into the mixture.

- Before you know it, your potion will be bubbling like mad!

Writer's Block

What a story! Can you find the two pictures that are exactly alike?

Design Your
PARK
PERFECTION

Build the most awesome park ever! What are you going to add? Draw it all in!

Design Your
SILLY THOUGHTS

What is this dude thinking? This dog just jumped on top of his head, out of nowhere! Fill out the thought bubble above his head.

Would You Rather...

Which would you rather do?
Look at each pair of options. Think about them and check the things you would like best. Ask your friends, too!

Would you rather be...

☐ The strongest person in the world   or   ☐ The smartest person in the world?

Would you rather...

☐ Have a million dollars right now   or   ☐ Be able to live forever?

Would you rather be able to...

☐ Speed time up?   or   ☐ Stop time **STOP**

Would you rather...

☐ Create an awesome video game   or   ☐ Invent a life-saving vaccine?

Let's Draw a
Chinese Dragon

On a separate piece of paper, follow these simple steps using a pencil and an eraser.

1 Draw a figure eight.

2 At the top part of the figure eight, draw a tail. Next, add two oval shapes to the circle for the dragon's snout.

3 Add arms, legs, and details to the face, as shown.

4 Draw flames. Add color and shadowing to give the dragon depth.

Are You Addicted To Video Games?

Do you spend a little TOO much time in a virtual world? To find out if you're a video game addict, read each statement, then put a check under "True" or "False." When you're done, go to the end of the quiz to see your results!

	TRUE	FALSE
1. I spend more than two hours a day playing video games.	◯	◯
2. The first thing I reach for when I wake up is my video game.	◯	◯
3. My mom often has to pry me away from my video games.	◯	◯
4. I know more about my fave video game than I do about my hometown.	◯	◯
5. I know the release date of every game coming out in the next year.	◯	◯
6. I can rock any video game even with my eyes closed.	◯	◯
7. I have reached the top level of at least ten games.	◯	◯

TRUE   FALSE

8. I can go days without stepping
   foot out of my room.

9. My dreams usually involve
   a video game.

TRUE

If you chose mostly "True" answers, you are addicted to video games, no doubt about it. It's totally cool that you are so passionate about your hobby. But, maybe once in a while, you could step outdoors and see what's going on in the real world, too!

FALSE

If you chose mostly "False" answers, you have your video game habit under control. No need to worry about it! You've done a great job of balancing video games and your social life.

Answers

Page 4
Construction Maze

Page 5
Brain Builder

1	4	6	7	5	3	9	2	8
2	5	3	4	8	9	7	1	6
9	8	7	1	2	6	5	4	3
6	3	5	2	7	8	1	9	4
7	9	1	3	6	4	2	8	5
4	2	8	9	1	5	6	3	7
5	6	4	8	9	2	3	7	1
3	1	2	5	4	7	8	6	9
8	7	9	6	3	1	4	5	2

Page 6
Tool Time

Drill	Sander
Hammer	Saw
Level	Screwdriver
Nail gun	Trowel
Pliers	Wrench

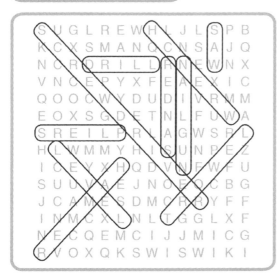

Page 7
Rockin' Rebus

B A S K E T B A L L

Answers

Page 11
Types of Ice Cream

¹S H E R B E T

³S P L I T

²S T R A W B E R R Y

⁴N E A P O L I T A N

⁵M I L K ⁶S H A K E

S A N D W I C H

⁷S U N D A E

ACROSS
3. Usually made with bananas
4. A mix of vanilla, chocolate, and strawberry
5. Made with ice cream, milk, and flavored syrup
7. Has a cherry on top

DOWN
1. A fruity ice cream made with only a little milk
2. A popular flavor of fruit ice cream
6. Vanilla between two cookies

Page 13
On The Lake

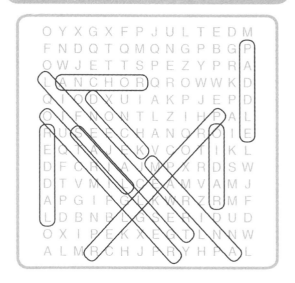

Anchor   Ladder   Marina   Paddle   Radio
Dock   Life jacket   Outrigger   Propeller   Sail

O Y X G X F P J U L T E D M
F N D Q T Q M Q N G P B G P
O W J E T T S P E Z Y P R A
L A N C H O R Q R O W W K D
Q I O D X U I A K P J E P D
O I F N O N T L Z I H P A L
R U S E E C H A N O R O I E
E Q T A I E K V C O T I K L
D F C H A J M P X R D S W
D T V M I C R E A M V A M J
A P G I F G I K W R Z R M F
L D B N B L G S E R I D U D
O X I P E K X E G T L N N W
A L M R C H J P R Y H P A L

Page 14
Scary Dragon

Page 18
Super Smart

3	2	1	5	8	4	6	9	7
7	5	4	6	2	9	1	3	8
6	9	8	7	1	3	4	2	5
8	7	5	9	4	2	3	1	6
9	4	3	1	6	5	7	8	2
1	6	2	8	3	7	5	4	9
2	8	7	3	5	1	9	6	4
5	1	6	4	9	8	2	7	3
4	3	9	2	7	6	8	5	1

Answers

Page 21
Ready For Rebus

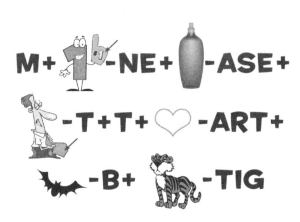

Page 24
Safari Animals

Page 25
Sundae Maze

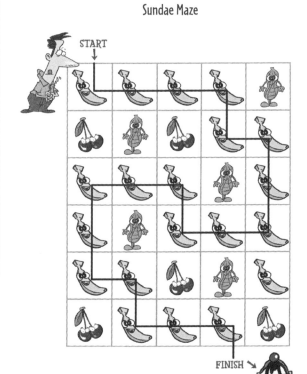

Page 27
School Trip

Answers

Page 29
Halloween Maze

Page 32
Super Fan

Page 33
Think Tank

9	3	4	7	6	1	5	8	2
2	8	7	9	3	5	4	6	1
6	1	5	8	4	2	7	9	3
4	9	3	1	2	7	8	5	6
8	6	2	5	9	3	1	7	4
5	7	1	6	8	4	3	2	9
7	4	9	3	5	6	2	1	8
3	5	6	2	1	8	9	4	7
1	2	8	4	7	9	6	3	5

Page 35
Zombie Attack!

Answers

Page 38
Baseball Star

Page 42
Action Figure

acorn	cure	once
acting	eating	orange
air	face	out
art	factor	rag
aunt	faint	range
auto	fern	ring
café	fig	rut
can	four	tear
cane	great	tie
car	groan	tiger
cite	icon	tiring
corn	ignore	tongue
cougar	ion	tragic
count	nag	train
crate	neat	true
cringe	ogre	tuna

Page 43
Family Portrait

Page 45
Decode-a-Riddle

W H A T   K I N D
T E X Q   H F K A

O F   E A R S   D O
L C   B X O P   A L

T R A I N S   H A V E ?
Q O X F K P   E X S B

E N G I N E E R S
B K D F K B B O P

Answers

Page 46
Video Games

Arcade   Console   Gamer   Keyboard   Role playing
Computer   Controller   Joystick   Programmer   Television

Page 48
Yummy Breakfast!

```
          ¹T 'O A S 'T E
    'B          M        T E
  'P A N C A K E S       A
    C           L
    O    'C E R E A L
    N           T
```

ACROSS
1. Cooked bread
5. Round, flat, and yummy
6. You usually pour milk over this

DOWN
2. Made with eggs and other ingredients mixed in
3. Some people drink this instead of coffee
4. A meat you eat with eggs

Page 49
Basketball Maze

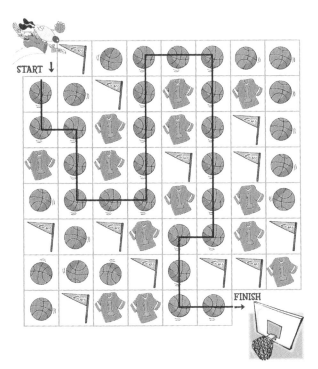

Page 51
Super Skater

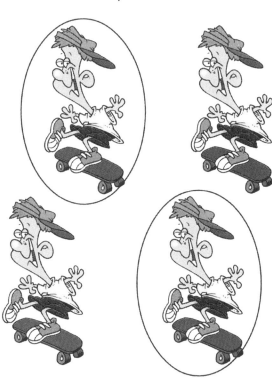

Answers

Page 54
Creature Feature

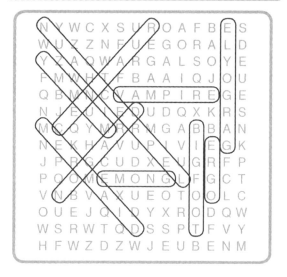

Page 58
Bouncy Castle

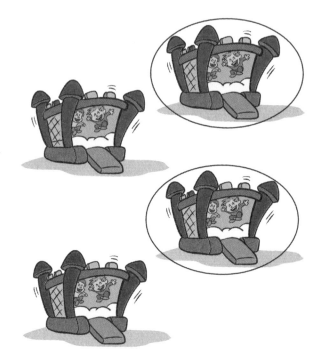

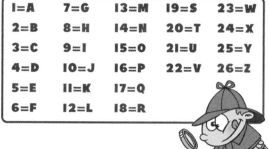

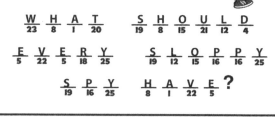

Page 59
Brilliant Brainiac

1	2	7	4	8	9	3	5	6
3	6	8	5	2	7	1	9	4
9	4	5	6	3	1	2	7	8
8	9	3	2	1	5	4	6	7
2	7	4	8	6	3	5	1	9
5	1	6	7	9	4	8	3	2
4	3	2	1	7	6	9	8	5
7	5	9	3	4	8	6	2	1
6	8	1	9	5	2	7	4	3

Page 60
Decode-a-Riddle

1=A	7=G	13=M	19=S	23=W
2=B	8=H	14=N	20=T	24=X
3=C	9=I	15=O	21=U	25=Y
4=D	10=J	16=P	22=V	26=Z
5=E	11=K	17=Q		
6=F	12=L	18=R		

W H A T — S H O U L D
23 8 1 20 — 19 8 15 21 12 4

E V E R Y — S L O P P Y
5 22 5 18 25 — 19 12 15 16 16 25

S P Y — H A V E?
19 16 25 — 8 1 22 5

A — L I C E N S E
1 — 12 9 3 5 14 19 5

T O — S P I L L
20 15 — 19 16 9 12 12

Answers

Page 61

Ups and Downs

S K A T E B O A R D

Page 65

Expedition

EXPEDITION

deep	ion	pint
den	need	pit
dent	net	point
diet	next	pox
din	node	teen
dine	note	ten
dip	one	tend
done	oxen	tide
edit	pen	tie
edition	pent	tied
end	pet	tine
eon	pie	tip
exit	pin	ton
expend	pine	tone

Page 72

Werewolf Maze

Page 73

Wacky Wizards

Answers

Page 79
Types of Knots

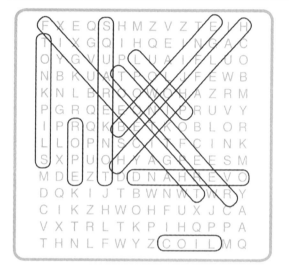

Page 80
Baseball Fever

Page 81
Helicopter Trip

HELICOPTER TRIP

cheep	hopper	propel
cheer	hotel	proper
chili	hotter	protect
chipper	otter	recipe
chirp	people	repel
citer	peril	reptile
clipper	piece	teeth
creep	piper	three
elite	pitch	treetop
erect	pitcher	tripe
ethic	poetic	triple
helper	police	tropic

Page 82
Rock and Roll

Answers

Page 84
Smart as a Whip

8	5	4	6	3	9	1	7	2
2	9	6	1	4	7	3	8	5
7	3	1	2	8	5	4	9	6
5	8	9	4	7	2	6	3	1
3	4	7	5	1	6	8	2	9
6	1	2	3	9	8	7	5	4
9	6	3	8	2	4	5	1	7
4	2	8	7	5	1	9	6	3
1	7	5	9	6	3	2	4	8

Page 85
Mixed-up Stories

1. After learning about coral reefs, Roberto asks his parents if he can take scuba diving lessons.

2. Roberto makes a scrapbook of pictures he took with a special under-water camera.

3. Roberto and his parents fly to the Bahamas to learn to scuba dive.

5
1
3
6
4
2

4. Roberto sees his favorite kind of fish, a parrotfish.

5. Roberto writes a report for science class and becomes interested in coral reefs.

6. Roberto and his parents get on a boat headed away from their hotel in the Bahamas.

Page 86
Explorer Maze

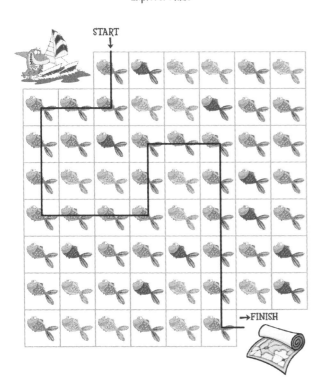

Page 87
Decode-a-Riddle

1=A	8=H	15=O	22=V
2=B	9=I	16=P	23=W
3=C	10=J	17=Q	24=X
4=D	11=K	18=R	25=Y
5=E	12=L	19=S	26=Z
6=F	13=M	20=T	
7=G	14=N	21=U	

W H A T   V E G E T A B L E
23 8 1 20   22 5 7 5 20 1 2 12 5

D O   Y O U   N E V E R
4 15   25 15 21   14 5 22 5 18

W A N T   T O   B R I N G
23 1 14 20   20 15   2 18 9 14 7

O N   A   B O A T?
15 14   1   2 15 1 20

A   L E A K
1   12 5 1 11

299

Answers

Page 90
Sports of all Sorts

Baseball Football Hockey Softball Tennis
Basketball Golf Soccer Swimming Volleyball

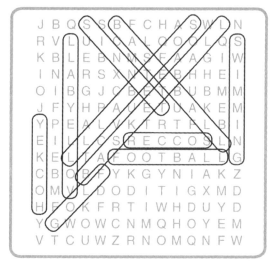

Page 93
No School Today!

```
¹S U M M E R
 N
²H O L I D A Y
 W
³S I C K
 T
⁴C O N F E R E N C E
 R
⁵M E E T I N G S
```

ACROSS
1. Season between Spring and Fall
2. Special type of "day" like Christmas or Easter
3. When you have a cold or toothache, you're ___SICK___.
4. When parents meet with teachers
5. Teachers go to these group events to discuss stuff.

DOWN
1. You do a lot of digging in these types of storms.

Page 98
Hockey Stuff

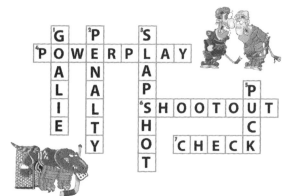

```
 ¹G  ²P     ³S
⁴P O W E R P L A Y
 A  E     L
 L  N     A
 I  A    ⁵P
 E  L  ⁶S H O O T O U T
    T     H     C
    Y     O  ⁷C H E C K
          T
```

ACROSS
4. This happens when one team has more players on the ice than the other.
6. This is used to decide the winning team; players take turns trying to score.
7. To do this is to bump another player out of the way.

DOWN
1. This player tries to keep the other team from scoring.
2. A player gets this if he violates a rule.
3. A hard-hitting shot at the goal from a distance away
5. This is what all the players scramble to get.

Page 99
Super Strength

8	2	5	3	4	9	7	6	1
9	1	3	8	6	7	2	4	5
6	7	4	5	1	2	8	9	3
5	3	1	6	9	8	4	7	2
7	8	2	4	3	5	9	1	6
4	6	9	2	7	1	3	5	8
1	4	6	7	2	3	5	8	9
3	5	7	9	8	6	1	2	4
2	9	8	1	5	4	6	3	7

Answers

Page 102
Birthday Party

Page 103
Out of This World

Earth	Mars	Milky Way	Pluto	Uranus
Jupiter	Mercury	Neptune	Saturn	Venus

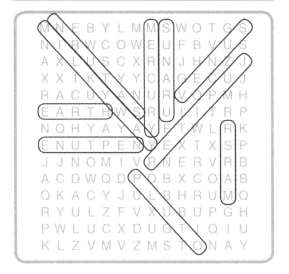

Page 104
Snow Day

Page 105
Out on the Lake

SAILING

301

Answers

Page 110
Decode-a-Riddle

1=A	7=G	13=M	19=S	22=V
2=B	8=H	14=N	20=T	23=W
3=C	9=I	15=O	21=U	24=X
4=D	10=J	16=P	25=Y	25=Y
5=E	11=K	17=Q		26=Z
6=F	12=L	18=R		

W H A T   D O   Y O U
23 8 1 20 4 15 25 15 21

D O   W I T H   A N
4 15 23 9 20 8 1 14

O L D   B I K E ?
15 12 4 2 9 11 5

Y O U
25 15 21

R E - C Y C L E   I T
18 5 3 25 3 12 5 9 20

Page 111
Ice-Cream Truck

Page 112
Puppy Maze

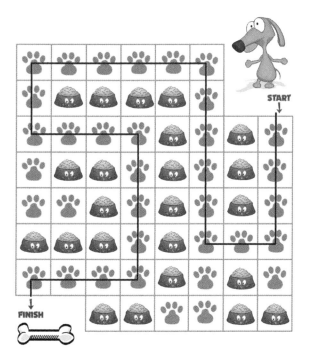

Page 113
Globetrotter

GLOBETROTTER

bet	globe	reel
beet	goo	robe
beg	greet	robot
belt	leg	roe
better	let	role
blot	letter	root
bog	lob	rot
bolt	lobe	tee
boot	log	toe
bore	lore	tore
bottle	lot	tote
eel	oboe	treble
getter	otter	tree
glee	rebel	trot

Answers

Page 114
Go, Go, Go

| Airplane | Car | Monster truck | Rickshaw | Wagon |
| Big rig | Helicopter | Motorcycle | Taxi | Yacht |

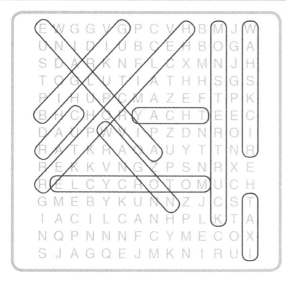

Page 115
Car Parts

ACROSS
2. Storage space in back
4. Helps the driver see around the car
7. Plays music
9. The "shoes" of the car
10. Needed for driving at night

DOWN
1. The "heart" of the car
3. Makes the car stop
5. Keeps everyone in the car safe
6. Lets other drivers know where you are
8. Pops out if there's an accident

Page 116
Dinosaur Maze

Page 118
Golf

| Ball | Club | Green | Par | Swing |
| Birdie | Course | Iron | Score | Wood |

Answers

Page 119
Cool Tree House

Page 123
Mixed-up Stories

1. Mark cooks some food in a special pot that hangs over his campfire.

2. Mark sets up his tent on the flattest spot.

3. Mark pours water over his campfire and stirs the ashes to make sure it is out.

4. Mark sweeps away any sticks and rocks so that his tent can lie flat.

5. Mark makes sure all his food is sealed up so animals don't bother him as he sleeps.

6. Mark gathers water to keep near his campfire, and small sticks to get the fire started.

<u>4</u> <u>2</u> <u>6</u> <u>1</u> <u>5</u> <u>3</u>

Page 126
"B" There or "B" Square

Bahamas Bangladesh Belgium Bolivia Brazil
Bali Barbados Bermuda Bosnia Bulgaria

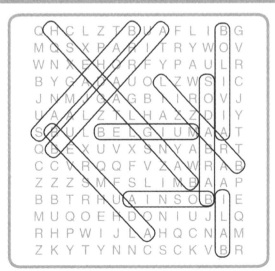

Page 127
Souvenirs

ACROSS
1. Dangles from a ring
3. Send this to a friend
5. Sticks to the fridge
6. Pull this over your head to show others where you've visited

DOWN
2. Goes on top of your head
3. Hang this on your wall
4. Be careful not to poke your finger with this!
5. Sip something from this

Answers

Page 129
Rebus Ruckus

 -W +D +

 -CAN + ↑

"SADDLE UP"

Page 130
Perfect Skills

6	5	9	4	1	8	2	3	7
8	7	3	2	6	5	1	9	4
1	4	2	9	7	3	6	5	8
5	8	4	7	2	9	3	6	1
2	9	6	3	4	1	7	8	5
3	1	7	5	8	6	9	4	2
7	2	5	6	3	4	8	1	9
9	6	1	8	5	2	4	7	3
4	3	8	1	9	7	5	2	6

Page 134
All About Yo-Yos!

Crossword answers:

- ¹L O O P T H E L O O P (down)
- ²F O R W A R D P A S S (down)
- ³W A L K T H E D O G (across)
- ⁴W I N D U P (across)
- ⁵G R A V I T Y P U L L (across)
- ⁶S L E E P E R (across)

ACROSS
3. A move where your yo-yo "walks" on the ground; 3 words
4. A move where you start with the yo-yo on the ground; 2 words
5. A move where you let the yo-yo hang before flicking it back up; 2 words
6. A move where you flick the yo-yo down and let it hang and spin

DOWN
1. A move where you don't catch the yo-yo and let it fling around; 3 words
2. A move where you release the yo-yo behind you, then pull it forward; 2 words

Page 135
Ahoy, Matey!

Answers

Page 136
Darts Maze

Page 137
Mixed-up Stories

1. A family listens to a tour guide talk about ancient ruins.

2. A family gets on a bus and takes their seats.

3. A family asks a tour guide to take their picture so they can always remember their trip.

4. A family wakes up in their hotel.

5. A tour guide asks if anyone has any questions.

6. A family arrives at the site of some famous ruins.

4 2 6 1 5 3

Page 139
Truckin' Around

Page 142
All-Star Hockey

| Assist | Goalie | Overtime | Pass | Puck |
| Breakaway | Interference | Pad | Penalty | Rebound |

```
B L O B I B N C M W M D S O
V P J E I X U C M K C U P P
E C N E R E F R E T N I L L
J P A S S Z W B U F E K G J
F H K G Z T P M Q Z P T R V
E Q A K Y A W A K A E R B E
K M A W D W B T D F B Q F Q
L Z I A R E B O U N D A L T
V B G T S N Y T L A N E P A
V R T O R S D C K A E W W Y
X R H Q A E I V S I C L J D
H I Z P F L V S X Q D D V Q
L A R M F N I O T D D J S Z
W B M F E L S E U P N F M H
```

Answers

Page 143
Fright Night

Page 148
Types of Spiders

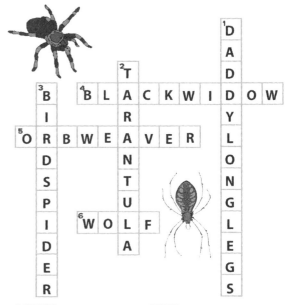

ACROSS
4. Very poisonous; 2 words
5. Named for its sphere-shaped web; 2 words
6. __WOLF__ spider; named after a fierce canine

DOWN
1. Named for the length of its limbs; 3 words
2. This type is sometimes a pet
3. Named for what it eats; 2 words (Hint: "It's a **BIRD SPIDER**, it's a plane!")

Page 151
Awesome Astronaut

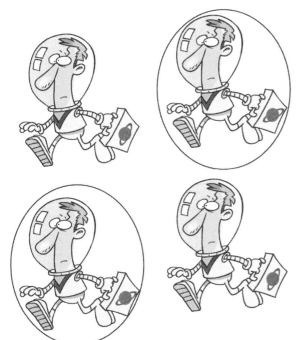

Page 152
Zoo Crew

Alligator Orangutan
Chimpanzee Polar bear
Elephant Rhinoceros
Giraffe Tiger
Lion Zebra

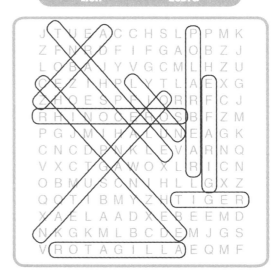

Answers

Page 153
Puzzle Power

4	1	3	6	7	8	2	5	9
6	8	2	9	3	5	7	4	1
7	5	9	4	2	1	6	3	8
3	9	4	5	1	6	8	2	7
1	7	5	8	9	2	4	6	3
8	2	6	3	4	7	9	1	5
9	3	7	1	6	4	5	8	2
5	6	1	2	8	9	3	7	4
2	4	8	7	5	3	1	9	6

Page 156
Blast Off Maze

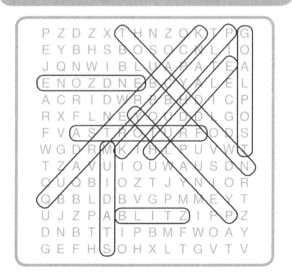

Page 157
Build It Up!

C O N S T R U C T I O N

Page 160
Football Fun

Astroturf　End zone　Huddle　Playbook　Stadium
Blitz　Goalpost　Penalty　Quarterback　Touchdown

Answers

Page 162
Roller Coaster

Page 163
Under the Big Top

ACROSS
1. Also known as the "Big Top"
4. A really big animal
5. Elephants eats these

DOWN
1. Acrobats swing from these
2. These performers have colorful clothes and big noses.
3. People walk across this, if they can balance.

Page 164
Rocking Numbers

6	5	9	4	1	8	2	3	7
8	7	3	2	6	5	1	9	4
1	4	2	9	7	3	6	5	8
5	8	4	7	2	6	3	6	1
2	9	6	8	4	2	7	8	5
3	1	7	3	8	6	9	4	2
7	2	5	6	3	4	8	1	9
9	6	1	8	5	2	4	7	3
4	3	8	1	9	7	5	2	6

Page 166
Ready, Set, Go!

Answers

Page 167
Creepy Crawlers

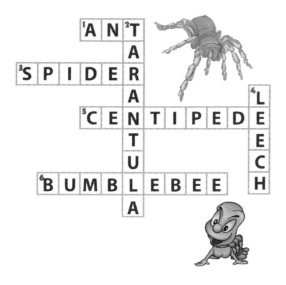

ACROSS
1. Digs a good picnic
3. Has eight legs
5. Has many, many legs
6. Has yellow and black stripes

DOWN
2. A hairy kind of spider
4. This type of worm sucks blood.

Page 180
Smart Math

1	8	4	6	3	5	7	2	9
6	2	3	7	8	9	1	5	4
9	5	7	2	1	4	8	3	6
3	4	1	8	9	2	6	7	5
7	9	2	3	5	6	4	1	8
8	6	5	1	4	7	2	9	3
4	1	6	5	7	3	9	8	2
5	7	9	4	2	8	3	6	1
2	3	8	9	6	1	5	4	7

Page 181
Let's Play!

M O N K E Y
B A R S

Page 182
Pinewood Derby

PINEWOOD DERBY

bed	dewy	open
bind	died	own
binder	done	peer
bone	drop	pine
bored	dry	pony
bow	dye	red
brie	end	rib
brown	ewe	ripe
brownie	ion	robe
deep	nerd	weed
deer	nod	weep
deny	one	weird

Answers

Page 184
Cool Cowboy

Page 188
Parks and Recreation

Aquarium	Hiking trail	Ski slopes
Beach	Lodge	Summer camp
Campsite	Museum	Zoo
	Park	

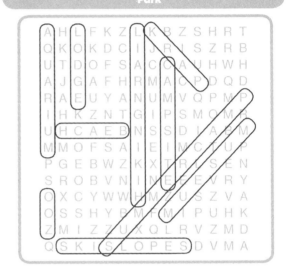

Page 192
Water-Balloon Fight

WATER-BALLOON FIGHT

anthill	eight	large
antler	faint	light
ballet	father	organ
ballot	fellow	rainbow
bangle	fiber	robin
baring	fight	their
bellow	finger	tiger
bigfoot	float	tight
bitter	gorilla	tower
boating	grill	train
bottle	heart	tribe
eating	hollow	weight

Page 194
Straight Up!

4	2	8	5	3	7	1	6	9
7	5	3	9	1	6	2	4	8
1	6	9	4	8	2	5	3	7
9	1	4	3	6	5	8	7	2
6	7	5	8	2	9	3	1	4
3	8	2	1	7	4	6	9	5
2	3	7	6	9	8	4	5	1
5	9	1	2	4	3	7	8	6
8	4	6	7	5	1	9	2	3

Answers

Page 195
Water Park

Page 196
Pool Maze

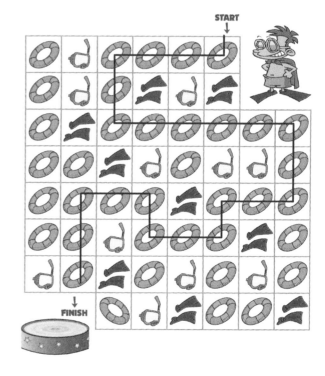

Page 197
Masked Ball

Page 200
The Great Outdoors

Answers

Page 201
Summer Camp

²G H O S T
³C
⁴C A M P F I R E
¹M A R S H M A L L O W
⁵T U B E
⁶C A N O
⁷B U N K
⁸C O U N S E L O R

ACROSS
4. Helps you cook things when you're out in the wilderness
5. You can float on the water in this
7. You might sleep in this
8. An adult who works at the camp

DOWN
1. You toast this over a campfire.
2. Tell this kind of story around a fire to spook the campers
3. Holds your water
6. Paddle this by yourself or with another person

Page 204
Types of Clothes

Hat	Jeans	Pajamas	Shoes	Socks
Jacket	Necktie	Shirt	Shorts	Trousers

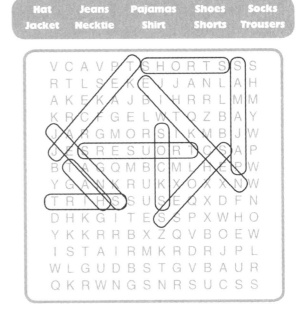

Page 208
Cat Maze

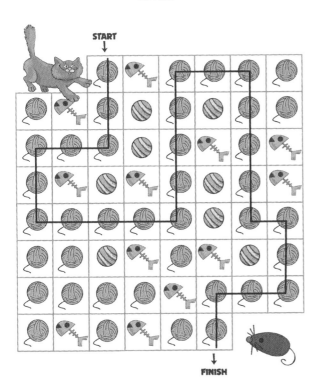

Page 209
Speedy Train

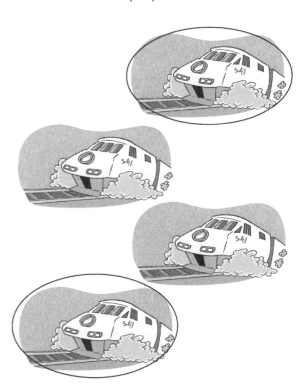

Answers

Page 212
Let's Party!

Balloons Cake Candy Friends Holiday
Birthday Candles Costume Gifts Sleepover

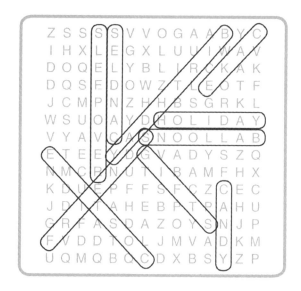

Page 213
What's Your IQ?

6	7	9	8	5	2	1	3	4
3	8	1	4	6	9	7	2	5
2	4	5	1	3	7	8	6	9
7	9	3	5	2	1	4	8	6
1	5	4	6	8	3	9	7	2
8	6	2	9	7	4	5	1	3
4	2	7	3	1	5	6	9	8
9	1	6	2	4	8	3	5	7
5	3	8	7	9	6	2	4	1

Page 217
Old West

Page 220
Shiver Me Timbers!

ACROSS
1. Pirates wear this on an eye
4. Another word for "my"
6. Sometimes pirates will give other pirates this type of "dot"
7. Weapon commonly used by pirates for defense
8. What pirates say when they see land
9. A pirate's main vehicle of transportation

DOWN
2. Means "yes"
3. This is shot out of a cannon
5. Some pirates have these in their ears

Answers

Page 224
Underwater Swimmer

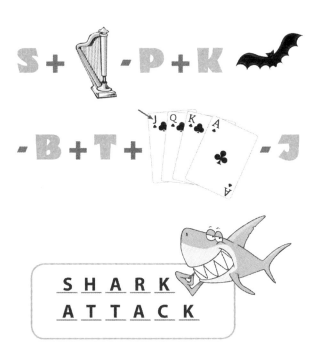

Page 225
Monster Maze

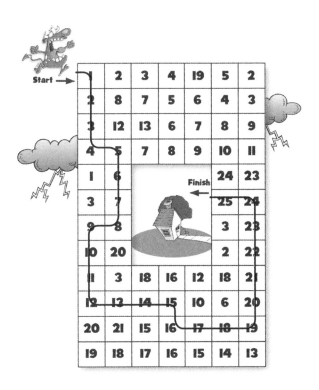

Page 226
Crime Fighter

Page 227
Camping

Backpack
Cabin
Campfire   Fishing   Sleeping bag   Tent
Campground   Ghost stories   Smores   Woods

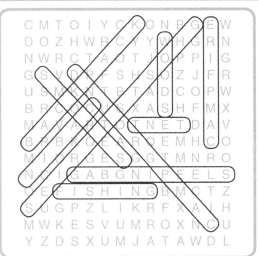

Answers

Page 236
Wet Weather

R A I N C O A T

Page 238
Road Trip

Page 242
Decode-a-Riddle

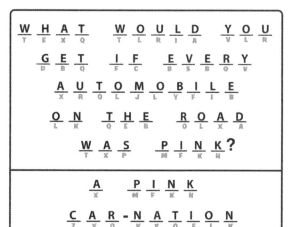

W	H	A	T		W	O	U	L	D		Y	O	U
Y	E	X	Q		T	L	R	I	A		V	L	R

G	E	T		I	F		E	V	E	R	Y
D	B	Q		F	C		B	S	B	O	V

A	U	T	O	M	O	B	I	L	E
X	R	Q	L	J	L	Y	F	I	B

O	N		T	H	E		R	O	A	D
L	K		Q	E	B		O	L	X	A

W	A	S		P	I	N	K	?
T	X	P		M	F	K	H	

A		P	I	N	K
X		M	F	K	H

C	A	R	-	N	A	T	I	O	N
Z	X	O		K	X	Q	F	L	K

Page 243
Into the Woods

Answers

Page 245
Super Solver

4	8	2	5	7	3	6	9	1
6	5	7	2	6	9	4	7	8
8	7	6	8	1	4	3	5	2
6	1	4	3	9	7	8	2	5
7	3	5	1	8	2	9	6	4
8	2	9	4	5	6	7	1	3
5	6	1	9	3	8	2	4	7
3	4	7	6	2	5	1	8	9
2	9	8	7	4	1	5	3	6

Page 247
Pool Party

Page 249
Winter Wonderland

F R O S T B I T E

Page 251
School Maze

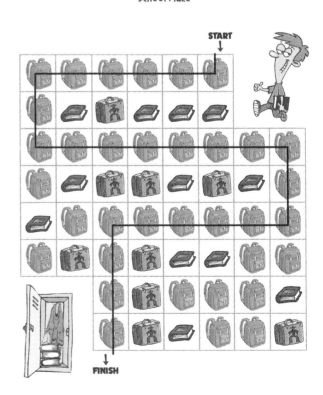

Answers

Page 254
Frenzy Fire Truck

Page 256
Construction Site

ACROSS
1. A big vehicle that hauls dirt
4. You dig this up; it's brown
5. You wear this to protect your noggin

DOWN
2. This makes concrete
3. This is used to build foundations
6. These pull up the dirt

Page 257
Magic Numbers

4	1	5	2	6	8	9	7	3
6	9	7	3	4	5	8	1	2
8	2	3	1	7	9	6	5	4
5	6	2	8	3	1	7	4	9
7	3	4	6	9	2	1	8	5
9	8	1	7	5	4	3	2	6
3	5	8	4	1	6	2	9	7
1	4	6	9	2	7	5	3	8
2	7	9	5	8	3	4	6	1

Page 261
Tricky Teammate

Answers

Page 263
Prehistoric Prey

Allosaurus	Pteranodon
Avimimus	Stegosaurus
Deinonychus	Triceratops
Iguanodon	Tyrannosaurus
Megalosaurus	Velociraptor

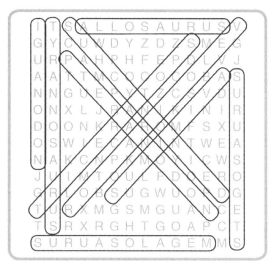

Page 267
Disaster Strikes

ACROSS
1. A tropical cyclone
4. The ground shakes
5. Looks like a funnel

DOWN
2. Might strong winds
3. Rocks and mud and debris tumble
5. Massively devastating wave

Page 271
Let's Jump!

DIVING BOARD

Page 272
Mixed-up Stories

3
4
1
5
6
2

Answers

Page 273
Sports Game

Page 276
Brain Scrambler

6	5	1	8	3	4	7	2	9
3	8	7	6	2	9	5	4	1
4	9	2	5	1	7	3	8	6
1	2	4	9	8	3	6	5	4
8	6	3	7	5	1	2	9	4
9	7	5	4	6	2	8	1	3
2	3	9	1	7	5	4	6	8
7	1	8	2	4	7	9	3	5
5	4	6	3	9	8	1	7	2

Page 278
Plain Batty Maze

Page 281
Writer's Block